Victorian Clocks

CLOCKS
of Every Description & Quality
CHIMING on BELLS or GONGS
True Westminster Note
Also on MUSICAL TUBES
Old-fashioned Clocks
Striking hours
& half hours
Chimney
Carriage
Regulator
Turret
Lever Clocks

DESIGNERS & MANUFACTURERS
of every style of CLOCK CASE.
TALL OLD ENGLISH & BRACKET
CHIPPENDALE SHERATON
CARVED OAK
Made in all particulars
according to pure
STYLE & FINISH
DIALS DESIGNED
to suit each clock
REPOUSSE
ENGRAVED
& CHASED

A & H. ROWLEY.

40 THEOBALDS ROAD ENGLAND

LONDON
All PARTS of CLOCKS with Bells
& Gongs included) and CLOCK
CASES made on the
PREMISES under strict
Personal supervision

We are constantly producing
NEW & ARTISTIC DESIGNS in
CASES & DIALS
Originality and Delicacy of Finish
being main
features

MOVEMENTS supplied WITHOUT CASES
WHEN SO REQUIRED

Victorian Clocks

Richard Good

British Museum Press

© 1996 Richard Good

Published by British Museum Press
A division of The British Museum Company
46 Bloomsbury Street, London WC1B 3QQ

A catalogue record for this book is available from the
British Library

ISBN 0 7141 0578 3

Richard Good has asserted his right to be identified as
the author of this work

Book design by Andrew Shoolbred
Jacket design by Roger Davies
Typeset by Create Publishing Services
Printed in Great Britain by The Bath Press, Avon

Front jacket: Detail of the dial of a Miniature Chiffonier
Mantel Timepiece by Thomas Cole, *c*.1850. See no. 51

Back jacket: A Year-Going Skeleton Timepiece with
Calendar and State of Wind Indicator, by John Pace,
c.1850. See no. 134

Frontispiece: Poster for the clockmakers Arthur
and Henry Rowley (see pages 12–13).

Contents

Introduction

*L*ittle has so far been written about the clocks of the Victorian era, that is 1837–1901. Until recent years most antiquarians considered that there was a natural cut-off date of about 1850, past which nothing could be considered worthy of attention. Everything changes and, inevitably, people have begun to collect items made after 1850, if only because things made before this date are becoming scarce and expensive. With some reluctance it was decided to make the requirement for an antique that it should be 100 years old. Then without warning people began to collect Art Nouveau objects. Where was it going to end! Well not there, for, with a growing nostalgia for the 1930s, Art Deco also entered the Sale Rooms. Dealers began to wonder if they should move to houses with large barns, since it seemed rash to throw away anything that had belonged to a previous generation.

Certainly Victoriana must be respectable if the plastic and chrome of the Art Deco period is acceptable. And indeed it is true that every age and style has its good and bad examples. Like Beethoven's music, however, it often needs the enchantment of distance to give the required detachment to appreciate what is the good and what is the bad. I hope you will find that in this volume there are many very fine objects. Of course, it must be admitted that there are some horrors, but even these examples are, almost without exception, well made.

Production

The beginning of the nineteenth century saw the mass production of pulley blocks for ships' rigging for the Navy. Later flintlock guns were made in America on an interchangeable basis. Good steel had been available since Huntsman had found how to manufacture it in the middle of the previous century. Maudsley made accurate screws for the control of machinery movements and for use in measuring instruments. Thus, providing the purchasing power was there, everything was set for a boom in the making of clocks and, in fact, they were to be made in this century in previously undreamt of quantities.

Victorian clocks

By the time Victoria came to the throne the population of the United Kingdom was about 20 million, a really large home market. The distribution of wealth was anything but even, however. A household servant might earn as little as £12 a year; Thwaites & Reed were paying their skilled clockmakers £1 15s. a week, while at the same time Vulliamy was making chandeliers costing as much as £1,000! A clock of the early period, say a striking clock with a rosewood case, (a popular wood of this time) and going for eight days might cost about 12 guineas, a 12 inch dial clock about 5 guineas; the latter would, therefore, cost an artisan almost a month's wages. Mid-nineteenth-century London was the richest city in the world and it is evident that whatever the better-off Victorians wanted, they had.

To give an idea of the wealth of the period a good example is Eaton Hall in Cheshire. In the 1880s the Duke of Westminster had the Hall rebuilt and the task was undertaken by Alfred Waterhouse, a well-known architect of the Gothic revival. Although no furniture was required Waterhouse succeeded in spending £600,000. Among other things an

Fig. (i) Frodsham Catalogue, 1897
We are fortunate that some catalogues have survived from the Victorian era, and one such is that of the prestigious firm Charles Frodsham, one of the big four in the nineteenth century. The others were Dent, Smiths and Thwaites & Reed.

As the title page says it is mainly about English clocks although some French clocks are included. We are luckily able to date this catalogue closely since it was in circulation just after Frodsham moved from 84, the Strand to 115, New Bond Street, which means a date of 1897. The picture on the back of the catalogue is of the premises at the Strand. What is written on the back of the catalogue is of interest for it gives details that make it only too clear what sort of a firm we are dealing with. The index shows that twenty-three entries were for English clocks and thirteen for French clocks. The most expensive standard clock is the English balance chime clock at 70 guineas! This is shown on page 25. Of course special clocks could be ordered. English carriage clocks are to be found at £47 5s., with a lever escapement.

The cheapest English clock is an ordinary English dial at 3 guineas, with a superior model costing 5 guineas. A striking version, at double the work, is double this price.

Browsing through this catalogue gives a good idea of the situation at the top end of the market.

Charles Frodsham & Co.,

Clockmakers by Appointment to the Queen.

Makers of Chronometers, Watches, Chronographs, Astronomical and other Clocks.
By Special Appointment to the Queen and T. R. H. the Prince and Princess of Wales ; Superintendents of Her Majesty's Clocks at Buckingham Palace.

Successors to Arnold, A.D. 1843 ; to Vulliamy, A.D. 1854 ; to W. Johnson, A.D. 1861.
Awarded the Admiralty Prize of £170 for excellency of Marine Chronometers.

The Telford Medal for C. F.'s Work on "The Isochronism of the Balance Spring."
First Class Medal at the Exhibition of 1851.
Gold Medal, Paris Exhibition, 1855.

Gold Medal of the First Order from the Emperor of Russia for services rendered to the great Russian Survey.
Medals of Honour as Juror at the International Exhibitions of London, 1862 ;
Dublin, 1865 ; Paris, 1867.   First Class Gold Medal, Naples, 1871.   First Admiralty Premium, 1871.
Commissioned by the Queen to make the Presentation Tower Clock for St. Mark's, Victoria Park, 1873.
Medal and Diploma, Philadelphia Exhibition, 1876.
Chronometers and Deck Watches purchased by the Admiralty at the Greenwich trials, 1882, 1884, 1885, 1887, 1890, 1891.

ONLY ADDRESS— **115, NEW BOND ST., W.**

84, STRAND, LONDON.

extravagant sum was spent on a 183 ft (55.8 m) clock tower, built to house a carrillon of twenty-eight bells that chimed 'Home Sweet Home'. In 1961 Eaton Hall was razed to the ground; only the stables, the chapel and, the reader will be glad to hear, the clock tower survive.

It should not be thought, however, that the Victorian era was one of unmitigated growth since there were at least two slumps in the property market in London and this, it is probably true to say, is an essential business barometer. The first occurred in the stock market crash of 1847. Luckily the Great Exhibition of 1851 lifted London out of the 1850s' slump and a boom occurred at the end of this decade. Growth continued until another slump came along in the 1880s.

Styles

As far as styles are concerned (when it is possible to make out any particular style) I suppose we can discern four particular influences; first the lingering influence of the Regency style, next the Egyptian (following Nelson's battle of the Nile), then there is the oriental style epitomised in the Royal Pavilion in Brighton and lastly the Gothic revival, the strongest influence of any in the Victorian era. The Gothic revival is what after all is responsible for the appearance of the most famous clock in the world, Big Ben (see the chapter on turret clocks for more information). The Egyptian influence was at its height in the 1810s but, as with all of these trends, it lingered on. It followed not only Nelson's victory but also the publication of Thomas Hope's *Household Furniture and Design* in 1807. Thomas Hope was a wealthy man who travelled extensively through Egypt, Italy and Greece. His designs, which were in the main for furniture, exhibit a blend of French Empire and English Romanticism. An example of one of Hope's designs is to be found in the King's Apartments in the Royal Pavilion: it is an ormolu and bronze mantel clock.

There was a growing interest in the Gothic style throughout the late eighteenth century, the dominant feature being the Norman arch. The great architect Thomas Hopper produced a Gothic masterpiece, namely Penrhyn Castle in Wales, now belonging to the National Trust. Building began in 1820 and finished in 1845. The castle is placed dramatically between Snowdonia and the Menai Strait and is generally recognised as being one of the finest buildings of its style and period in Britain, notable for its wealth of carving. The Victorians had a great weakness for carving and their rosewood and mahogany clock cases were frequently embellished in this way. Thomas Hopper also built a Gothic conservatory for the Prince Regent at Carlton House. Such major projects had their impact in every sphere of the decorative arts.

Towards the end of Victoria's reign the Empire style was also revived, and it was this that was to characterise the Edwardian period, giving a welcome lightness to furniture after the somewhat heavy Gothic influence.

Victorian craftsmanship

Whatever one's opinion of design during the Victorian era no one can dispute the superlative craftsmanship of the period. As today, of course, the best cost the most but when one paid for the best it is difficult to see how the quality could have been bettered. The best castings, for instance, would probably be difficult to match today despite all of the technical advances that have been made during the century that has passed.

The reason for this high quality is that the size of the market required an enormous pool of craftsmen to satisfy it and those that rose to the top were outstanding. The apprentice system was still very much alive and skills were often passed from father to son for generations. Of course rubbish was made – you could get a dozen cheap musical boxes for a shilling – and one dreads to think of the living standards of those who made them.

It is true that some of the perfection stemmed from the extreme specialisation that existed. Some unfortunates made just one particular component for the whole of their lives – no wonder they were good at it. The grind of making the same component for twelve hours a day six days a week, fifty-two weeks of the year from the age of twelve until one dropped dead hardly bears contemplating. This was not necessarily the worst of it either, since some of the jobs destroyed health. The men who did fire gilding, for instance, often ended up in the madhouse through breathing in the poisonous mercury vapour. Hatters used mercury in their processes, hence the saying 'mad as a hatter'. When we think nostalgically of the past it is perhaps as well to remember these things.

It is not surprising that advances in timekeeping continued to be made in the Victorian era; there was in fact a constant improvement on the technical side. Much will be said later about the aspects concerned with precision in clocks and especially in chronometers.

Although giant steps had been made by the horological masters of the seventeenth and eighteenth centuries, the mechanical timekeeper still had some way to go before perfection could be claimed. In fact this was never to be the case with mechanical timekeepers for it was to be the atomic clock that claimed this distinction – perfect because it itself is taken as the standard of timekeeping.

Collecting Victorian clocks

It is no longer true to say that Victorian clocks can be bought cheaply. However, it is true to say that they are good value for money. It is also true that in general they are a safer clock to buy than earlier examples, for they have not been messed about with to the extent that earlier clocks have. Fakes are relatively rare. However, some clocks have been made as replicas and are now being passed off as genuine and the reader is referred particularly to the chapter on skeleton clocks for details of this.

Another advantage of Victorian clocks is that they are not as worn as the earlier examples tend to be. The first and most obvious reason for

Fig. (ii) Arthur and Henry Rowley, 1860–1902
We are lucky that this superb poster has survived. It is now housed in the British Museum and I thank them for permission to publish it. In Britten the Rowleys are recorded as being first at 67 Red Lion Street, Clerkenwell from 1860–9, and afterwards at Grays Inn Road and then Theobalds Road. As can be seen from the illustration the actual address was No. 40. Arthur died in 1900 aged 85 and Henry in 1902 aged 75. We know that this advertisement was after 1885 since a clock is shown on the right with tubular gongs which do not appear until that date. (Tubular gongs were patented by Harrington in 1885.)

In case the legends are not clear when this poster is reproduced they are as follows: On the left top: 'CLOCKS of every description and quality, chiming on bells or gongs true Westminster. Note also on MUSICAL TUBES. Old fashioned clocks striking hours and half hours. Chimney Carriage, Regulator, Turret and lever clocks.' On the right top: 'DESIGNERS & MANUFACTURERS of every style of CLOCK CASE. TALL OLD ENGLISH & BRACKET CHIPPENDALE SHERETON CARVED OAK made in all particulars according to pure STYLE & FINISH. DIALS DESIGNED to suit each clock REPOUSSE ENGRAVED & CHASED.'

In the middle is the address and below the following: 'All parts of clocks with bells and gongs included and CLOCK CASES made on the premises under strict personal supervision. We are constantly producing NEW & ARTISTIC DESIGNS in CASES & DIALS. Originality and delicacy of finish being main features.' At the bottom is: 'MOVEMENTS SUPPLIED WITHOUT CASES WHEN SO REQUIRED.' The poster is signed J.Rt.J. Brown.

In the centre, where the Mother is showing the boy the long case clock, the piece on the chest is a sand glass.

Looking at it from our point of view it is a bit terrifying to learn that any style of clock or *movement* could be copied. How many of their reproductions are now accepted as genuine?

this is that they are not as old, but a second reason is that they tend to be very well made with particularly solid plates.

There are exceptions to this, the domestic long case clock being a prime example. They have often been run into the ground simply because they will continue to go long after the time has passed when they need to be serviced. After having been patched up to keep them going with the minimum of expenditure they have reached the stage today when only the most major of overhauls will get them going again. This can be a very expensive business and allowance needs to be made for this possibility when a purchase is being contemplated. However, a small long case clock (6 ft 6 in (2 m) or less) may be a desirable acquisition just as a piece of furniture even if it does not go!

The name on the clock

There are few problems more vexing than the question of ascribing a clock to a particular firm or maker. Except where it is glaringly obvious that both case and movement have come from abroad (however the clock may be signed) examples are usually assumed to be by the signatory. To realise the futility of delving further let us examine what the 'maker' may have done:

1. He may have bought a complete clock to his own specification.
2. He may have bought in a clock of a standard type.
3. He may have bought a finished mechanism and cased it.
4. He may have bought a partly finished mechanism, finished it and cased it, either himself or by buying in a case.
5. He may have made a complete clock mechanism and then bought in a case.
6. He may have made both the mechanism and the case.

All of these products will bear the 'maker's' name and their quality will be chosen or controlled by him (or her).

It may or may not be possible to determine the precise mix of circumstances that resulted in the creation of the finished clock. Often it is not particularly important to do so, the name and very often the address, really being required mainly to help to date the item and to put it into context.

Tracking down a name There are three standard works detailing makers: they are Baillie, Britten and Loomes (see the Bibliography). The latest edition of Britten's *Old Clocks and Watches and their Makers* is very strong on London makers, having been brought up to date recently from records held at the Guildhall. Baillie details makers not always covered by Britten but only up to about 1850. Loomes covers the makers not in Baillie and although he has often drawn on other and more fully detailed sources we are not told what these are.

When dates are given in these books it is not always entirely clear what these mean. A single date may be that of a hall-mark found on a watch bearing an individual maker's name. Two dates may have been obtained from two hall-marked watches or from trade directories. In general Britten tries to tell you the source of the information. Both Baillie and Britten give a lot of other information if it is known. In general the information in Loomes is skimpy but the book is still essential since, especially with later makers, it is the only source. For much more detailed information it is best to refer to books on horology in a specific area and details of these may be found in the Bibliography. Unfortunately the whole of Britain is not covered, nor is it likely to be in the lifetime of anybody reading this book.

Technical details

For additional technical information, see Appendix B in R. Good, *Keeping Time*, published by British Museum Press, London, 1993.

1 English Carriage Clocks

*E*nglish carriage clocks were produced in much smaller quantities than those in France and in general were of a very high standard. Unlike the vast majority of French clocks, which had going barrels, the English clocks almost invariably had fusees with chains.

Most of the clocks had lever escapements, but later firms such as Dent, Frodsham and Kullberg sometimes used the chronometer escapement in their top-of-the-range models. Some clocks, especially those made by Dent, were so large and heavy that they could not really be considered portable and therefore are not strictly carriage clocks.

Like skeleton clocks, these clocks provided an opportunity for the craftsman to show off his work, because the mechanism is usually fully visible; although there are some clocks where the case is not glazed (except, of course, at the front).

Although the majority of English carriage clocks were made in London during the Victorian era, some were finished locally by firms such as Roskell of Liverpool. These latter are not made to the same standard as the best London pieces.

It is not easy to date English carriage clocks as styles changed comparatively little during the Victorian age. Furthermore, rough movements were supplied to 'makers' by specialist firms, the 'maker' being in reality a finisher who was able to assemble a clock using a combination of case/dial/hands obtained from a variety of workmen. Often the firms involved in marketing the clocks were long-lived and, luckily for us, seemed to have a great liking for frequent changes of address. These can often be of great assistance in dating, using the trade directories of the day.

If only more workbooks had survived we would be better off, but only those of Vulliamy, Dent, Frodsham, Usher & Cole and Kullberg remain.

It is a curious fact that the urge towards an undue amount of decoration, so typical of the Victorian era, did not affect the design of carriage clocks except in so far as engraving was concerned. This, however, does not offend the sensibilities and carriage clocks were among the first type of Victorian clock to command prices that were comparable with their quality.

The English began to make carriage clocks in about 1820 so that by Victorian times they were well into production. Charles Allix, in his definitive book on the subject, remarks that many Victorian gentlemen had what amounted to a mania for punctuality. Samuel Smiles (1812–1904, and thus a true Victorian) quotes Louis XIV's favourite motto, 'Punctuality is the politeness of Kings' but goes on to add 'It is also the duty of gentlemen, and the necessity of men of business.' This is certainly one explanation of the popularity of the carriage clock. At first they were not large and thus eminently suitable for transporting around. Later they became bigger and one could be forgiven for thinking that, in fact, they were not moved at all, so heavy were they. However, nothing was thought of large amounts of heavy luggage (after all, the owners themselves did not have to carry it). Also, the clock was provided with a carrying box, often a work of art in its own right; some of these will be found illustrated, with their clocks, below. In these padded boxes the clock could be safely transported and could also be consulted easily since a removable panel revealed a 'window' through which the clock dial was visible.

There are clocks in this section that have wooden cases. It is not clear whether these were considered to be carriage clocks when they were first made. It is possible that they were considered as merely one variety of mantel clock. However, since they are so like carriage clocks in every other way, I decided to include them in this section.

1 *Carriage Clock*

by J.F. and T. Cole, 1823
See colour plate I

This clock is included (despite the fact that strictly speaking it is too early to be called Victorian) because it is the precursor of all the carriage clocks in this section. It is the earliest datable English carriage clock and one of its two makers, Thomas Cole (the brother of James Ferguson Cole, the other), is responsible for a style of clock that takes up the whole of Chapter 3. The style of this clock, the humpback, was originated by A.L. Breguet around 1813 and J.F. Cole became known as 'the English Breguet'.

The clock is cased in silver and hall-marked London 1823. It has grande sonnerie striking on two gongs and one mainspring drives both trains.

There is a fly-back date hand working over a sector showing 31 days. On either side of the centre is a subsidiary dial showing the day and the month. Above the sector is a moon dial. Below the XII is the subsidiary seconds dial with sunrise and sunset within. The subsidiary dial below the main dial is for the alarm. The winding square is on the right and the hand set square on the left, just below the bezel. The platform has a lever escapement with the lever and escape wheel beneath the platform. The remarkable escape wheel is of steel and the teeth are both slotted and drilled to help retain the oil. All the lift is on the teeth of this escape wheel. The compensation balance has a double roller and the balance spring has an overcoil.

H. 7¹/₂in (19.1 cm).

Courtesy British Museum

2 *Quarter-Striking and Repeating Carriage Clock with Alarm*

by Barraud & Lund, London, 1893

The case is of mahogany and has unusual inset brass corners on the moulded base which stands on flat brass bun feet. The case is glazed all round. The silvered brass dial is boldly engraved with Roman numerals and at the VI there is a subsidiary alarm dial. The blued steel hands do not appear to be original.

On the dial is the inscription:
BARRAUD & LUNDS 14, BISHOPSGATE ST. CORNHILL LONDON.

One cannot help but wonder at the misspelling of the name Lund.

The movement has triple chain fusees and strikes the quarters on two gongs. It is provided with a strike/silent facility.

Measurements not available.

Barraud & Lund 1838–1929
They were originally at 41, Cornhill London. In 1889 they moved a few doors higher (see *H.J.* October 1889). In 1893 they moved to 14, Bishopsgate Street Cornhill.

The company exhibited at the Great Exhibition of 1851 and also at the International Exhibition of 1862 when they won a medal. They invented an electrical system of synchronising public clocks.

3 *Month-Going, Minute-Repeating, Alarm, Perpetual Calendar Carriage Clock*

by Viner, *c.* 1850

The case is of walnut with a brass carrying handle and a fretted back of brass.

The 4 in (10.2 cm) diameter dial of engine-turned silver inscribed *Viner Invt et Fecit 235 Regent St London*. The dial has a subsidiary seconds dial at XII and up and down dials showing the state of wind of both springs at III and IX. There is a moon dial at VI.

Beneath the main dial, which has a gilt surround, are four more subsidiary dials showing the day, date, month and the bissextile (leap-year). The calendar work is perpetual.

The movement is month going and quarter striking with minute repeating and an alarm. It has twin fusees. The striking train fusee is reversed. The platform escapement has a spring detent escapement but the balance and spring are not original. The minute repeating is controlled by a specially modified watch movement. (This method was later to be used in the twentieth century by the Swiss to provide minute repeating in carriage clocks.)

The main striking and chiming is on two large spiral gongs and the alarm on a bell. The minute-repeating watch movement has its own two gongs. The movement is signed *Viner* (at the bottom left-hand side of the back plate) with the address *235 Regent St. London* (at the right-hand side).

It is not possible to date this clock closely but it was probably made about 1850 since Viner was on his own from 1844 onwards and left the Regent Street address in 1855.

Thos Mudge is the first English maker known to fit minute repeating to a watch that can be dated. The first minute-repeating clock was probably that by A.L. Breguet (No. 262) which predates Viner's clock by about twenty years. Minute repeating was of value during the hours of darkness or to a blind person since the time could be determined to the nearest minute with a touch of the finger.

Viner would probably have considered his clock as his 'chef d'oeuvre'; such a complex clock is impressive by any standards. One cannot help but admire the ingenuity shown in fitting watch work to a clock to achieve the desired result; quite possibly Viner was the first to do such a thing.

H. 9 in (23 cm); W. 7 in (18 cm); D. 6 in (15 cm).

The well-known maker *Charles Edward Viner* was born in 1788 and was apprenticed to Thos Savage in 1802. Free of Clockmakers' Company in 1813 and was made a Liveryman in 1819. His businesses in the Victorian era were at:

3

8 Sweetings Alley Cornhill 1816–40
233 Regent Street 1826–35
235 Regent Street 1836–55
(where this clock was made)
82 Old Bond Street 1844–57
19 Sackville Street 1856–67
158 New Bond Street 1868–9

Viner was in business alone 1814 to 1823 and 1844 to 1869; between 1824 and 1835 he traded as Viner & Hoskins, and between 1826 and 1843 as Viner & Co. He died 7 June 1875.

---

4 *Timepiece Carriage Clock*
by J. R. Arnold/Chas Frodsham, No. 989,
c. 1860

'Milestone' gilt-metal case engraved with flowers and scrolls on a hatched ground with a two-piece folding handle.

Silvered dial with centre similarly engraved to case, gothic numerals, signed *Chas Frodsham, 84 Strand Clockmaker to the Queen*, on the chapter ring. Fleur-de-lis blued steel hands. Dial with florally pierced mask. Up and down dial below six o'clock. Movement with fusee and chain and platform lever escapement. Signed on the back plate *Arnold's Chas. Frodsham 84 Strand London, 989*.

H. 5 in (12.7 cm).

Case possibly by F.W. Robin. See J.B. Hawkins, *Thomas Cole*, 1975 p. 168 and illustration p. 171.

4

5

5 Striking and Repeating Carriage Clock

by Carter of Cornhill, *c.* 1870

This elegant clock has a gilded case of Corniche style although the base has not got the usual relief. The handle has a fluted centre with ogee ends. The repeating push piece is on top of the case. A most unusual dial for this type of clock consists of an enamelled chapter ring with a heavily engraved centre and surround. The hands are of blued steel and of moon design. Below the six is a scroll carrying the signature *CARTER 61 CORNHILL*.

The twin chain fusee movement has a platform with a ratchet tooth lever escapement. The hours and the half-hours are struck and repeated on a gong. Hand set and winding is from the back.

H. 7¹/₂ in (19 cm).

John Carter was at 61 Cornhill from 1840 to 1878. He was a Fellow of the Royal Astronomical Society from 1830 and a Fellow of the Society of Antiquaries from 1852. He was a juror at the Paris Exhibition of 1855 and Lord Mayor of London in 1859. He was also Master of the Clockmakers' Company twice, in 1856 and 1859.

6

6 Carriage Timepiece

by Vieyres, Pall Mall, London, *c.* 1840

A gilt case, the front and back flanked by fluted pilasters. A flat top with a cast handle with floral ends and an engraved centre. Plain turned finials. A silvered dial, its centre florally engraved. Blued steel moon hands. The dial is set in an engraved mask, on this mask beneath the six is a putto with a garland of flowers. On the sides in floral surrounds are vases of flowers standing on balustrades. The top and bottom of the central part of the case is patterned with a type of herringbone design. The flat top of the case is also engraved.

The chain-fusee movement has a platform with a duplex escapement and is signed on the back plate *Vieyres Pall Mall London*. The use of

the duplex escapement is most unusual in English work. See also no. 22.

H. 5 in (10 cm).

Anthony Vieyres 1829–75, was at Pall Mall 1832–47. He was one of the directors of the ill-starred British Watch Co.

7 A Grande Sonnerie 8-Day Striking and Minute-Repeating Carriage Clock with Tourbillon

by Nicole Nielsen & Co., 14 Soho Square, London *c.* 1900

The case and dial Perhaps one of the most magnificent types of carriage clock ever made. The case in this particular example is of base metal with silver rims and a glazed door to the back. Other examples of this type of clock have silver cases and differing complications. Set into

7

is signed *Nicole Nielsen & Co. 14 Soho Square London*, and is by Willis. The hands are all of blued steel, the hour and minute being of fleur-de-lis pattern. The two subsidiary dials are up-and-down dials for the chain fusees which can be seen in fig. 7b. Only two trains are used despite the complexity of the striking arrangements.

The movement　The plates are finished frosted gilt and are to chronometer standard, as indeed is all the work.

The movement is signed, as is the dial, but additionally has the number *11558*. Both the striking and going sides have chain fusees with maintaining power. The striking is on gongs which can be seen in fig. 7a starting from the left-hand side of the curved portion and disappearing behind the right side of the bottom portion of the movement. Although the work as far as the centre is very like that in a marine chronometer, the work from then onwards resembles nothing so much as large watch work. The system of striking and repeating (fig. 7b) is based on that in the Viner clock (see this section p. 19) but instead of being watch size as it is in the Viner clock it is scaled-up to suit clock practice. It is because of the use of this type of mechanism that only one barrel is required to both repeat and strike, including the refinement of minute repeating.

This clock is one of the finest of a small family of similar clocks with tourbillons all made (whatever name they bear) by Nicole Nielsen, the only makers in England to produce a series of both watches and clocks with tourbillons.

The tourbillon　The tourbillon can be seen most clearly in fig. 7a. It consists of a frame that contains the balance and escapement and in this example rotates every minute. The purpose of the device, invented by the horological genius A. L. Breguet, is to eliminate the errors caused when the escapement and the balance and spring assume different positions in the vertical plane. For many decades watches with tourbillons swept the board in the Observatory competitions. Not only is the device useful but the rapidly rotating ones especially are fascinating to watch in action. They exercise the skill of the horologist to the

the glass door (fig. 7a) are three dust caps, the centre one marked *SET HANDS* and the other two with the direction of wind, necessary because each is different. I think this has been done to achieve symmetry of layout of the set up ratchets, an attention to detail that is quite astonishing.

There is a carrying handle and in front of this is the repeat button which when pressed causes the clock to strike the hours, quarters and minutes past the quarter. On each side of this button are controls for strike/silent on the right and grande/petite sonnerie on the left.

The main enamel dial and the two enamel subsidiary dials have an engine-turned silver surround. The main dial shows the hours and minutes and has a sunk subsidiary seconds dial; it

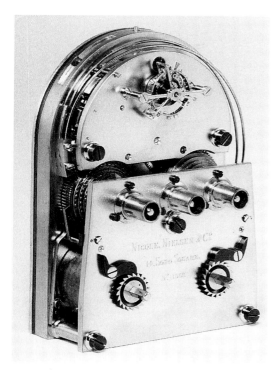

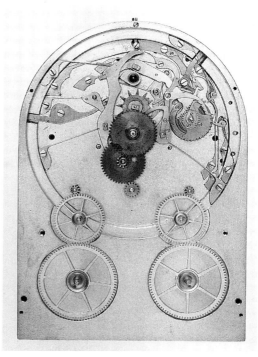

Fig. 7a The movement removed from the case. The beautiful tourbillon is seen on the back of the upper stage of the movement. The lower half has the signature and houses the barrels and the fuses.

Fig. 7b A view under the dial disclosing the fact that the striking and repeating work is strictly watch type scaled-up in size.

extreme and represent the pinnacle of craftsmanship when made well.

Height 5¹/₂ in (14 cm).

Seven of these clocks are known; all are grande sonnerie and two also have perpetual calendars.

The firm of *Nicole Nielsen* resulted from the coming together of two remarkable men, Adolphe Nicole and Emil Nielsen.

Adolphe Nicole had a business at 80b Dean Street from 1841 to 1858 when he moved to 14 Soho Square. In 1844 he patented keyless work and chronograph work with a heart-shaped cam. In 1862 he patented improved chronograph work with a castle wheel. In this same year he was a medallist in the 1862 Exhibition.

Emil Nielsen married Nicole's daughter, and was for many years the head of the firm Nicole Nielsen. They supplied all the foremost houses of the day. In 1889 a

visit was organised to their factory in Soho Square which was written up in the July issue of the *H.J.* of the same year. It is obvious from what was written that everything was made under the same roof using the most sophisticated methods. Although making standard watches, their speciality was making complicated pieces to special order. Latterly Nielsen was closely connected with Frodshams and after the latter's death in 1871 became a director of that company.

Nielsen died in 1899 but the factory was kept going by R.B. North. The famous name of Nicole Nielsen died in 1917 when they changed their name to North & Sons. Then in 1922 they turned to making speedometers and car clocks and the heyday of English watch and clockmaking came to a close.

In 1932 the firm was forced into liquidation. For a fuller account of the history of Nicole Nielsen and R.B. North's involvement, see *The Frodshams* by Vaudrey Mercer (Ticehurst, 1981).

8 Quarter-Striking Carriage Clock

by James McCabe, London, No. 2927, *c.* 1860

Gilt and engraved case with canted corners, 'beaks' at top and ogee mouldings at the base. The engraved dial is gilded so as to contrast in colour with the case. Dial engraved *Jas McCabe Royal Exchange London 2927*.

Fleur-de-lis hands almost certainly by Peter Pendleton, hand makers of Prescot, Lancashire.

Movement with chain fusees, quarter striking, lever escapement and compensated balance. Finished throughout to chronometer standard.

H. 9³/₄ in (24.8 cm).

One of the most beautiful examples of an English carriage clock ever to be made. Illustrated in Allix p. 280.

8

9 Striking and Repeating Carriage Clock

by James McCabe, Royal Exchange, No. 2871, *c.* 1856

The clock still has its brass-bound mahogany travelling box. A gilded Anglaise case. The dial is silvered, the hands are of blued steel and of fleur-de-lis pattern.

The movement has twin chain-fusees; it strikes and repeats on a gong. There is a strike/silent control. Inscribed *JAMES MCCABE ROYAL EXCHANGE LONDON 2871*.

The platform has a lever escapement and this has a plain three-armed balance. The original numbered key is still with the clock.

H. 7¹/₄ in (18.4 cm).

This clock was illustrated in the *A.H. Journal*, Summer Edition for 1980 on p. 132 and is courtesy of J. Carlton Smith.

Some McCabe clocks can be dated and thus give a clue as to the dates of others:

> 2735 has a presentation inscription of 1851.
> 2850 is dated 1855.
> 2916 has a dated certificate 1857.
> 3140 has both mainsprings signed and dated March 1866 R. Smith.

9

10 *Giant Carriage Clock with Perpetual Calendar, Equation of Time, Moon Work, Grande-Sonnerie Striking and Repeating, with four gear trains and a Chronometer Escapement*

by M.F. Dent, London, No. 24128, *c.* 1862

The case of this giant clock is of gilded brass and of Corniche style. The dial is also of gilded brass and is engraved all over. There are five subsidiary dials. The seconds dial is below the XII and above the main dial on the left is the day of the week, on the right the date and in the middle the month dial; marked around this dial is the equation of time. Within the month dial is the moon dial and below it the 4-year cycle.

The hands are of blued steel, the hour and minute hands being Breguet style. Above the VI is a cartouche with *M.F DENT. Chronometer Maker TO THE QUEEN 33 & 34 Cockspur St. CHARING CROSS, LONDON, 24128.*

Engraved on the front of the base is: *TO H. CUSTANCE from THE DUKE OF HAMILTON Oct. 1879.*

10

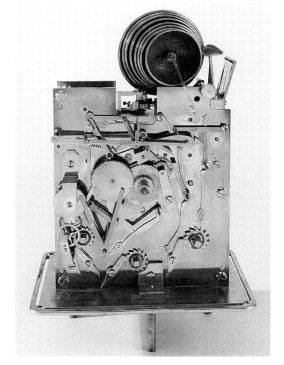

Fig. 10a (above right) Under the dial plate showing the striking work and the platform. The chronometer-style balance is visible with its helical spring.

Fig. 10b (right) The dial sub plate with the calendar work. The cam for the equation of time work can be seen in the middle.

The movement is quarter chiming on eight bells striking the hours on a gong. It repeats Grande Sonnerie. It has three trains with chain fusees; they are reversed fusees. The plates are held together by four pillars with large polished steel screws at both ends. The perpetual calendar work is, most unusually, mounted on the dial plate, the only connection being through a pin and fork. This calendar work is driven by its own barrel so that the going train is not required to do any work in changing the date.

There is a large platform with a chronometer escapement and a compensation balance.

This clock was exhibited by Aspreys at New Bond Street. The exhibition ran from 26 November to 17 December 1975. There were 87 exhibits and 20 of the clocks were British. This clock was Cat. No. 75 and is illustrated in the catalogue which was published at the time of the exhibition, entitled *Rare Carriage Clocks*.

Height 18½ in (47 cm) with the handle up. The weight is an astonishing 58 lb (26.3 kg)!

Three other giant carriage clocks by Dent are known; their numbers are 23470, 23715 and 25262. The clock numbered 23470 was almost certainly made in 1861. Clock 23710 was made in 1862. Clock 25262 was probably in the International Exhibition of 1867, although there is no proof of this.

M.F. Dent were at Cockspur Street between 1856 and 1875.

11 *Carriage Timepiece*
by J. & A. Jump, London, No. 115, *c.* 1865

The gilt case is glazed only at the front; not even the top is glazed. There is engine-turning around the base and the frieze and the rest of the case is engraved. Both the handle and the pilasters are fluted. The engine-turned silvered dial is inscribed *JUMP* in a small cartouche under the XII. The dial has a gilt surround which is also engine-turned.

The chain-fusee movement has a platform with a lever escapement. The movement is also signed *J. & A. Jump Old Bond St. London No 115*. (Not all Jump clocks are numbered.)

H. 4½ in (11.5 cm).

This clock is discussed in Allix p. 290, plate IX/77.

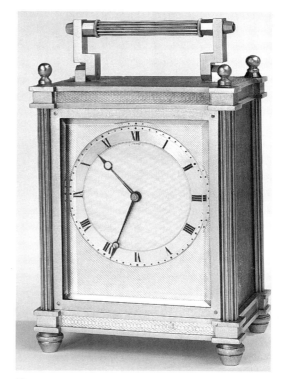

11

Joseph & Henry Jump were at 1a Old Bond Street, from 1856 to 1871, and known to have been at the same place in 1875. From their headed notepaper it can be seen that they were at 55 Pall Mall, opposite Marlborough House shortly before 1887 when they had moved to 11 Old Bond Street. From this invoice (fig. 11a) it can be seen that to have a customer's clocks wound for a year cost a guinea. The bill was presented two and a half years after the customer had died, the invoice being sent to the executors!

Fig. 11a

12 Quarter-Striking Humpback Silver Carriage Clock with Calendar and Phases of the Moon

by Jump, London 1889

A humpback case of silver hall-marked London 1889, with a carrying chain. An engine-turned mask to the dial and an engine-turned dial, both silver. A subsidiary seconds dial below the XII and above the VI, a moon dial showing the phases and age of the moon. Below the main dial are two more subsidiary dials showing, on the left, the days of the week and, on the right, the date. Between the two is the nameplate with *Jump London*. Below this is a rectangular aperture with the month.

The gold hands are of Breguet style, the moon dial is enamelled on gold. The other three hands are of blued steel.

The calendar work is not perpetual.

The movement has a platform with a ratchet tooth lever escapement.

Measurements not available.

The first of this type of clock was made by Jump before 1883. Its design is based on that pioneered by A.L. Breguet. See Allix p. 289 and plate IX/76 for a similar example.

Allix tells us that in a letter from Mr A. Haydon Jump (the great grandson of R. Jump) he says that 'the first of these clocks was made for Lord Ashburton. It cost the firm a load of money . . . . My father presented the bill to Lord A. with trembling hands and apologised for the high charge. Lord A. took the bill and wrote out a cheque at once *for double the amount charged on the bill!!!* and expressed his appreciation.'

Richard Jump is said to have been a servant to B.L. Vulliamy in 1812 (Britten). In 1825 his son Richard Thomas was apprenticed to Vulliamy and his other son Joseph similarly apprenticed in 1827. They remained with Vulliamy until he died in 1852. In 1856 J. & A. Jump were at 1a Old Bond St. This was probably Joseph and Alfred. In 1875 the firm became Joseph & Henry. Joseph died in 1899 but the firm still carried on.

13

13 *Striking and Repeating Carriage Clock*

by E.J. Dent, London, No. 8293, *c.* 1850

An Anglaise type case with a band of fluting below the top. The enamel dial has a pierced gilt surround engraved with scrolling leaves and flowers. The dial is signed *E.J. Dent London*.

The repeating button is, unusually, at the side of the case.

The movement has twin chain fusees and a platform with a lever escapement and a compensation balance. There is a strike/silent facility. The back plate is signed *Dent, London 8293*.

H. 9 in (23 cm).

This clock was probably made shortly before the death of E.J. Dent in 1853. Vaudrey Mercer in his book on Dent (1977) comments that it is difficult to date his carriage clocks from their numbers (see p. 678).

14

15

14   *Carriage Clock*

by F. Dent, 61 Strand and 34 Royal
Exchange, London, No. 1458, *c.* 1853

This clock is of interest because it is the only one
recorded that bears this name. The dial is
inscribed: *F. DENT 61 STRAND & 34 ROYAL
EXCHANGE LONDON 1458.* F.W. Dent were
at this address from the death of E.J. Dent in
1853 until 1860.

E.J. Dent's stock was then divided between
Frederick and his brother Richard and it would
seem that they applied their names to the old
stock. See Vaudrey Mercer's *Edward John Dent*, p.
677.

Measurements not available.

15   *Striking and Repeating Carriage Clock*

by McMaster & Son, Dublin, No. 367,
c. 1860

Rosewood case glazed all round and on top, with
moulded base and cheese feet. Gilt carrying
handle.

Square dial aperture with unusually engraved
silvered dial, the engraving protruding between
each of the chapters. The dial inscribed *McMaster
& Son Dublin No. 367*, moon hands.

On top of the case, to the right, the repeating
button. On the side on the left a hard/soft lever.

Twin chain-fusee movement repeating, at will,
the substantial lever platform escapement with
compensated balance. Striking on a gong. The
movement similarly signed to the dial.

H. 9¼ in (23.5 cm).

16   *Eight-day Chronometer Carriage Timepiece*

by John Poole, London, No. 4428, *c.* 1855
See colour plate II

Gilt case of Anglaise style with large observation
glass at the top and glazed all round.

The dial silvered and engine-turned with
subsidiary seconds with *CHRONOMETER*
engraved above the up-and-down dial. In a
cartouche below the chapter ring *JOHN POOLE
57 FENCHURCH STREET LONDON 4428.*

High quality blued steel fleur-de-lis hands,
probably by James Hood.

The movement, which is clamped between the
case elements, (not screwed in position) is of very
high quality. Both back and front plates are
finished by snailing. High count train, jewelled
throughout and fitted with endstones. Chain
fusee with Harrison's maintaining power. Very
large platform with Earnshaw-type spring detent
escapement, bimetallic compensated balance
with Poole's auxiliary and a blued steel helical
spring. Heavily engraved balance cock with large
endstone. Invented or rather re-invented
independently by John Poole in about 1845 his
form of auxiliary was widely and successfully
used.

H. of clock 9 in (23 cm).

John Poole gained first position in the Greenwich trials
in 1845 with a trial number of 21.0. He exhibited at
Paris in 1855 where he obtained a Bronze Medal,
possibly for this very clock and again in London in 1862
where he again won a medal. A marine chronometer of
his is at present in the Collection of the Clockmakers'
Company.

John Poole was at Fenchurch Street from 1856 to
1875.

17 Miniature Chronometer Carriage Clock, No. 847

by Charles Frodsham, 84 Strand, London, 1851

Silver case with rear door and winding hole shutter, hallmarked *London 1851*. Divided and collapsible carrying handle, and block feet. Circular enamel dial signed *Chas. Frodsham 847 AD Fmsz* with silver mask engraved with scrolls and foliage.

Chain-fusee movement with spotted plates signed *Chas Frodsham 84, Strand*. Sunk gilt platform with spring-detent escapement, free-sprung compensation balance with blued steel helical spring.

H. 4 in (10 cm).

Fitted travelling case, lid with key compartment. This piece was probably made for the Great Exhibition of 1851.

17

18 Striking and Repeating Carriage Clock

by James McCabe, No. 2916, with oak travelling case, 1857

Bronzed Anglaise case glazed on the front, sides and top, with a ribbed handle. The oak travelling case is lined in blue velvet and with brass corners and flush-fitted handle, removable shutter at the front, Brahmah lock, sprung and latched key compartment.

Silk lined flap in the lid.

$2\frac{3}{4}$ in (7 cm) silvered dial with inscription *JAMES McCABE ROYAL EXCHANGE LONDON 2916* and blued steel fleur-de-lis hands.

Twin chain-fusee mechanism with lever escapement and compensation balance. Striking and repeating on a gong.

The certificate which accompanied the clock, (fig. 18a) reads as follows: 'This is to certify that the accompanying Clock described below and named James McCabe, Royal Exchange, London, No 2916 was made by us and Sold to Messrs. Richardson Bros. London, 30th April 1857 (signed) McCabe & Co. Chronometer Watch & Clock Makers'; the case, movement and dial are then separately described in manuscript; a printed note reads: 'The Practice of Surreptitiously affixing our Name to very inferior Watches (chiefly for the India Market) having increased to a great extent we have deemed it expedient for the protection of the Public & our own reputation to adopt the above precaution.'

Fig. 18b shows the invoice from Richardson Brothers (late J.M. Richardson) of 23 Cornhill, dated 30 April 1857 and addressed to Lieutenant Charles Elliot, which reads: 'To a small size eight day spring Carriage Clock in round cornered bronzed Metal Case with glass sides and top, lever escapement, silvered dial plate, steel chains, repeating & striking hours on finely toned gong etc. name Jas McCabe Royal Exchange London No. 2916 33 12 (£33 12s.), complete with Morocco Travelling Case.'

The missing part of the invoice may have referred to the surviving oak travelling case, which is contemporary and almost certainly original.

Above **18**; right **Fig. 18a**; below right **Fig. 18b**

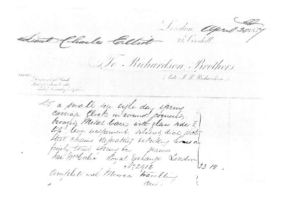

In the 1856 City of London Directory Richardson Brothers of 23 Cornhill are listed as booksellers.

McCabe No. 2850 bears a presentation inscription dated 1855. This suggests a rate of production of between thirty and forty clocks a year.

19 *Repeating Carriage Clock*
by Dent, London, No. 598, *c.* 1845

An ebonised case of rectangular form with fluted bands and a gilded carrying handle. A plain outset base with bun feet. The repeating button is at the side not on top of the case. The circular white enamel dial is inscribed *Dent 82 Strand London* and has a pierced and engraved foliate mask. Blued steel moon hands. Twin chain fusees, a platform with a ratchet tooth lever escapement with an underslung lever. A compensation balance. The movement striking the hours. The back plate with a strike/silent lever and inscribed *Dent 82 Strand London No. 598.*

H. 8½ in (21.6 cm).

19

20 *Repeating Carriage Clock*
by Dent, London, No. 581, *c.* 1844

The main differences between this clock and the previous clock are that the mask around the dial is not pierced, there is an additional layer on top of the clock and there are no fluted bands. On this clock the dial itself is also numbered.

Measurements not available.

20

21 *Quarter-Striking Carriage Clock*
by Grohe, London, *c.* 1860

This clock has a glazed rosewood case with a gilt handle (for a similar clock see that by Dent on p. 29; it is almost certain that Dent also made this clock). Below the top moulding is a band of

21

22 Quarter-Striking and Repeating Carriage Clock with a Duplex Escapement

by Dent, No. 13261, *c.* 1855

A bronzed case with a plain outset base and a reeded top. The silvered dial is engine-turned and has a pierced and engraved gilt mask. A plaque above VI bears the inscription *Dent No. 13261*. The Breguet-style hands are of gold.

The movement has triple chain-fusee and is quarter striking on two bells, the hour strike being on a gong. The back plate is plain and is signed as is the dial. There is a platform with a compensated balance and, most unusually, a duplex escapement. See also no. 6.

H. 9 in (23 cm).

22

fluting. There is a moulded outset base with bun feet.

With the clock is a leather-covered wooden carrying case.

The sight ring to the dial is, unusually, engraved. The rectangular dial is engraved all over except for the circular chapter ring which is 5 in (12.7 cm) in diameter. Below the six is a cartouche which bears the signature *GROHE WIGMORE STREET LONDON*. The blued steel hands are of fleur-de-lis design.

The movement has twin chain-fusees and the back plate is engraved, as the dial. The quarter striking is on gongs. The platform has a ratchet tooth lever escapement and a bimetallic compensation balance.

It was possible to order a clock identical in appearance to this but three train and with a chronometer escapement. No doubt it would have cost twice as much.

H. 12 in (30. 5 cm), a large clock.

James Grohe was the successor to Charles Haley, a very well-known maker. He is recorded in business between 1832 and 1867.

The duplex escapement is not to be found in any English carriage clock recorded in Allix. There are examples, but they are in clocks that originate elsewhere.

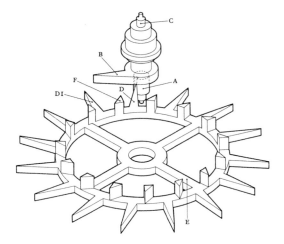

Fig. 22a. The Duplex Escapement
A is the locking roller, this has a groove that, as the balance rotates in an anticlockwise direction and at the correct moment, allows the locking tooth **D** to pass and the escape wheel **E** to move forward. The upstanding tooth **F** on the escape wheel **E** impulses the pallet **B** on the balance staff **C**. As the balance continues to revolve the tooth **DI** will come to rest against the locking roller **A**. On the reverse swing of the balance the tooth **DI** will fall into the notch but will almost immediately be lifted back onto the full diameter of the roller, so that there will be no action, thus this is a single beat escapement.

23 *Chronometer Carriage Clock*

by J. Sewill, Liverpool, Glasgow & London, c. 1880

An Anglaise gilt brass case with dentilled decoration and a reeded handle and reeded pilasters. A moulded surround to the engine-turned mask which surrounds the enamel dial. The dial is inscribed *SEWILL MAKER TO THE ROYAL NAVY LIVERPOOL GLASGOW & LONDON*.

The blued steel hands are of spade design.

23

The movement has spotted plates and the pillars are screwed at both ends. There is of course a chain-fusee and an Earnshaw spring detent escapement. The compensated balance has a blued steel helical spring.

A truly elegant clock, English work at its best.

H. 9¼ in (23.5 cm).

Sewill were first at 61, South Castle Street, Liverpool and are now at 20, Britannia Pavilion, Albert Dock, Liverpool. Their name is now Sewills and they advertise themselves as 'Makers to the Admiralty Estd. 1800 AD'.

24 *Quarter-Chiming Carriage Clock*

by Smith & Sons, Clerkenwell, London, *c.* 1845

A plain case that defies classification but is nearest in style to an Anglaise case. A large clock with a florally engraved dial with below the VI a cartouche bearing the name *SMITH & SONS CLERKENWELL LONDON*. Blued steel fleur-de-lis hands.

The three-train chain-fusee movement has quarter striking, a platform with a lever escapement and a compensation balance.

H. 14 in (35.6 cm).

There was another of these clocks in the Exhibition of Rare Carriage Clocks put on by Aspreys in 1975, see the Exhibition Catalogue entry No. 79.

John Smith & Sons were first established in 1780 and by 1830 had a factory in St John's Square, Clerkenwell, where they remained until a few years ago. They do not make clocks any more, being suppliers of raw materials, especially non-ferrous.

24

They made clocks of every variety from the smallest timepieces to the largest turret clocks and were accounted in 1851 as being among only half a dozen clock manufacturers on such a large scale. There was a piece about the firm in the *Illustrated London News* published 20 September 1851 which went on to say that the majority of the clock trade was based on

small masters employing for the most part only two journeymen or apprentices who attend to particular branches of their trade. For instance, the dial enamellers, the hand makers, the pinion maker, the wheel cutter, the fusee cutter, the movement maker, the spring maker, the pendulum and barrel maker, the carver, the case maker, the clock glass maker, the French polisher and finisher, so that when a clock of a particular construction is ordered of one of the masters, he has to depend upon a dozen workmen living in various parts of the district for the several distinctive portions of the work required to complete the clock. Delay after delay is the consequence. 'The wheel cutter is so engaged,' or 'the case maker has deceived me,' and such like are the many reasons, and so, disappointing some anxious inventor of some horological improvement.

It is quite obvious, therefore, that a factory which embraces all the various branches of the business must possess considerable advantages especially when all the operators are housed under the immediate superintendence and practiced [*sic*] eye of the principals.

Our attention was lately directed to such an establishment in St. John's Square, Clerkenwell, belonging to John Smith & Sons, which occupies the site of the once famous clock manufactory of Colonel Magniac. One of the principals kindly attended to us during an entire day which we spent in examining closely the various operations necessary in producing a clock, and also several beautiful machines employed in facilitating some of the more tedious processes.

There are then details of the brass foundry:

We find that the sand used for taking the cast was taken from Hampstead Heath, mixed with loam taken from the same locality. All the various pieces of brass required for the construction of a clock could be cast at the same time. The brass finishing shop was for the making of dials, pendulums, forging hammers, brazing, soldering, pullys (*sic*), repeating work, and wheel-cutting machines. Buhl work of brass and

Right **Fig. 24a** John Smith & Sons: a view of the works.

Centre left **Fig. 24b** The casting shop.

Centre right **Fig. 24c** The case making shop.

Bottom **Fig. 24d** The machine shop.

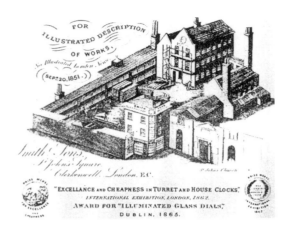

mother o' pearl was produced on a machine called 'neddy', clock rings or bezels and turret clocks all around.

There is one machine in this department which especially attracted our attention, and that is called a fusee engine by which the spiral groove is cut in the solid brass intended for the fusee. The brass is put upon a steel arbor placed between two centres – the operator with his right hand presses a triangular sliding bar, furnished at the end with a steel cutter against the brass, whilst with his left hand he turns a handle in connection with a sliding frame on which is a brass bar, placed at a given angle, so as to regulate the size of the spiral groove. This bar is adjusted by means of a segment at either end. By this machine the grooves of the fusee, of from three quarters of an inch to the largest size required, are readily cut.

After visiting the various manufacturing departments of the establishment, we were finally conducted to the showrooms which contain an extensive assortment of eight-day skeleton clocks representing various ecclesiastical edifices. Some striking the hours on a cathedral-toned gong and others chiming the quarters on eight bells. Then there are oak, mahogany, and rosewood [cases], both carved and plain, many of elaborate designs, and all produced by this establishment.

Nor are these clocks solely for the English market but also for China, Turkey, and other parts of the world, as we discovered by the curious characters on the dials, answering to our numerals.

Smiths produced a catalogue in 1865 which illustrates their truly amazing range of clocks. An outside illuminated dial for watchmakers, railway stations and public buildings commenced at £25. Fillery's detector clock with half-hour bell and double dials was £7. A skeleton clock representing Litchfield Cathedral, best quality, was £9; a quarter-striking skeleton clock was, however, upwards of £20; for these prices skeleton clocks came complete with base and glass shade. All of their wooden cases were made on the premises. They were already at this time offering raw materials, also brass work, clock springs, dials and clock wheels in sets, fusees, springs, barrels, clock chains, steel and iron work, gut lines, clock hands, winders, keys, pendulums, superfine prepared watch oil, watch glasses of every description and mahogany watch glass boxes. They also advertised glass shades of every description 'for covering and protecting all articles liable to injury by exposure'.

25   A Carriage Timepiece
Anonymous, c. 1840

They did not always get it right! Beautiful though the work may be on this clock, with its lovely engraving, somehow the proportions are all wrong. The dial is too small for the clock, the handle is all squashed up and the cartouche in the middle of the richly engraved mask to the dial is partly disappearing behind the base of the case.

The dial is silvered and the painted numerals have been redone and badly at that.

The movement has a chain fusee and a platform with a ratchet tooth lever escapement.

H. 7 in (17.8 cm).

Critical though I may be of certain aspects of this clock it seems amazing to me that so much loving craftsmanship can be lavished on a clock and yet nobody takes the trouble to sign it.

25

2 Marine and Domestic Chronometers

By the time Victoria came to the throne all of the fundamental advances had already been made in the design of chronometers. What remained was the troublesome 'Middle Temperature Error' (referred to from now on as M.T.E.).

The solution lay in the development of new spring materials, but to start with a bewildering array of balances were made to act with the steel balance spring. This work was carried out almost entirely by English makers, not least because the English dominated the chronometer field during the nineteenth century.

These compensation balances were often of great complexity and required the finest of craftsmen to construct them. Sometimes, in fact, the only person to make a success of a particular balance was the inventor himself, the only one who had sufficient incentive to overcome the problems involved!

Many of the attempts to solve the problem led to the making of balances that were not as stable as they needed to be. Others were too expensive for general use. There is a fine collection of many different types of these specialised compensation balances in the British Museum and they are fully described by this author in Volume 6 of the *Catalogue of Watches in the British Museum* (1989).

Reference is made in the section on exhibitions to the many balances on show at the 1862 Exhibition.

Although the vast majority of chronometers were for use at sea or for surveying purposes they were also used domestically. Sometimes a standard movement was put into a special case when the balance would run vertically, not good practice. At other times the chronometer was made more like a large carriage clock with the balance on a platform and hence horizontal. In fact it is true to say that only a fine dividing line separates the two types of timepiece, marine and domestic. Despite this, there is never really any doubt about each individual example.

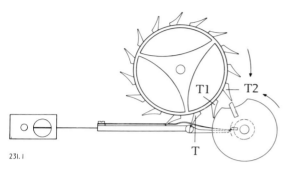

231.1

Fig. (iii) The Chronometer Escapement

In the diagram the tooth **T** is locked on the stone of the detent. The discharge stone on the small roller is just picking up the detent spring and is about to move the detent aside until the tooth **T** is able to pass the detent and in doing so the tooth **T2** will give impulse to the balance by pushing on the impulse stone on the large roller. Meanwhile the discharge stone has passed the detent and the detent has returned smartly to its banking (not shown in the diagram) in time to stop the tooth **T1**. On the return swing of the balance the discharge stone picks up the detent passing spring and is able to move it aside without disturbing the rest of the detent. This is because in this direction the full length of the spring is acted upon whereas in the other direction the spring rests against the horn of the detent and such a short length of spring is available for deflection that it might as well be considered as one with the detent.

Although the balance only gets impulse at every other vibration the escape wheel makes a revolution in just the same time as if it was maintained by a lever escapement which gives impulse at every vibration. This is because the wheel moves forward by a full tooth space at each impulse whereas with the lever escapement it only moves forward a half-tooth space. In this diagram the detent is machined from the solid and is called a foot detent.

In the next figure the detent is built up from several components, here impulse is just coming to an end and the escape wheel is just about to lock again.

Each time a chronometer is turned upside down in order to wind it there is a possibility that its rate will be disturbed. This is simply due to the fact that the disposition of the oil is altered as the pivots move in their bearings. Because of this there were attempts to make chronometers keyless with varying degrees of success. One of the designs that was to prove satisfactory is that illustrated in the *H.J.* for May 1888, pp. 134–5.

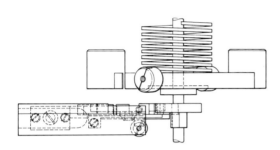

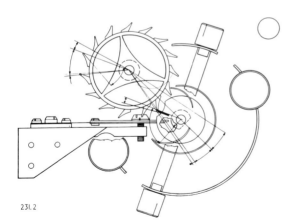

231.2

Fig. (iv) The Greenwich Chronometer Trials for 1853 (overleaf)

These records are of great interest, for instance, they give details of the type of temperature compensation used and contain the results for the Loseby chronometer that is described on pp. 49–51. Unfortunately, it is by no means easy to interpret these records. One chronometer may be very stable throughout its test but not very good in extremes of temperature. Another may drift continually but be reasonably predictable in what it does. Frodsham, one of the best chronometer makers of this period, had to take one of their chronometers away because of its behaviour, this was No. 2484.

The chronometer by Wieland, also taken away and returned after a fortnight, proved never to be very good in extremes of temperature despite the optimistic description of its compensation.

The temperatures shown are, of course, Fahrenheit and range from 22 degrees to 105. During 8 of the 26 weeks of testing the chronometers were put outside of a North window, for 12 weeks they were indoors and for 6 weeks they were in a gas oven.

NAME OF MAKER.	Number.	Whether Pocket, 1, 2, or 8 Days.	Construction of Escapement and Balance, from the description furnished by the Maker.	(I.)—WEEKLY SUMS OF DAILY RATES									
				Jan. 8—15 *	Jan. 15—22 *	Jan. 22—29 *	Jan. 29 to Feb. 5 *	Feb. 5—12 *	Feb. 12—19 *	Feb. 19—26 *	Feb. 26 to Mar. 5 †	March 5—12 †	March 12—19 †
Lister and Son.......	508	2	Auxiliary compensation to the balance, as in former years.	− 3·1	− 0·9	− 1·0	+ 1·5	+ 1·8	+ 3·5	+ 4·7	+13·3	+ 9·1	+ 9·
Poole..............	1585	2	Auxiliary compensation to the balance, as in former years.	−14·1	−13·1	−14·8	−13·0	− 9·0	−12·5	− 9·9	+ 1·4	+ 1·6	+ 2·
Woolf	5237	2	Auxiliary compensation to the balance, acting at low temperatures.	....	+ 5·9	+ 6·6	+ 7·5	+10·0	+ 9·4	+ 8·6	+ 7·0	+11·2	+14·
Loseby	126	2	Loseby's patented auxiliary mercurial compensation to balance.	+ 2·0	+ 4·5	+ 5·9	+ 8·1	+ 9·8	+14·7	+13·8	− 1·4	− 8·0	− 6·
Dent	2375	2	Dent's patent balance: see pamphlet, "On the Errors of Chronometers," p.23.	....	+17·4	+15·1	+13·5	+15·7	+15·7	+ 9·6	+17·2	+21·8	+23
C. Frodsham........	2484	2	Ordinary construction.	−11·1	−14·3	−20·7	−21·0	−17·9	−25·1	−21·6	− 2·1	− 8·3	− 7·
Reid and Son	1092	2	Auxiliary compensation to the balance, acting at low temperatures.	....	−11·7	−14·3	−16·1	−14·7	−14·7	−11·6	−24·0	−26·3	−25·
Glover..............	275	2	Auxiliary compensation to the balance, somewhat differing from Eiffe's.	+ 5·2	+ 7·9	+ 7·0	+ 6·1	+ 7·0	+ 0·5	+ 4·4	− 2·0	− 3·0	+ 4·
Hewitt and Son	1999	2	Eiffe's auxiliary to balance, with a small original alteration.	−35·0	−38·5	−40·0	−35·9	−42·7	−54·4	−49·8	−40·0	−39·3	−35·
Dixon	380	2	Auxiliary compensation to the balance, unpublished.	....	−26·3	−22·6	−17·3	−16·0	−11·1	−10·6	+ 5·6	+ 7·0	+ 9·
Lawson.............	1152	2	Auxiliary compensation to the balance, acting at low temperatures.	....	−28·9	−31·7	−30·7	−29·6	−32·4	−34·9	− 4·1	+ 4·0	− 2·
Eiffe............	482	2	Eiffe's auxiliary to balance by application to pendulum spring, as in former years.	....	−13·1	−18·8	−19·5	−18·7	−22·9	−21·1	+14·7	+16·7	+19·
Hewitt..............	1520	2	Eiffe's auxiliary to balance, with a small original alteration.	−21·6	−24·4	−31·3	−35·2	−34·0	−44·8	−40·2	−23·6	−27·4	−26·
M'Clellan	148	2	Auxiliary compensation to the balance, at extreme temperatures.	+23·3	+16·5	+12·5	+11·5	+21·2	+27·7	+31·8	+29·1	+29·7	+29·
Parkinson and Bouts..	850	2	Ordinary construction.	−15·0	−19·1	−20·4	−11·5	−11·5	−21·0	−16·5	− 1·9	− 3·3	− 0·
Carter	535	2	Ordinary construction.	....	+ 6·4	+ 1·9	+ 0·3	+ 4·3	+ 8·0	+ 4·0	+23·3	+22·7	+25·
Wieland	788	2	Balance with auxiliary compensating lever, acting throughout every change of temperature, to counteract the variation of the pendulum spring.	....	....	....	....	....		−22·3	− 0·1	−47·9	−47·
Chorley.............	851	2	Some improvement in the construction of the balance.	+ 6·3	+ 1·7	− 5·5	− 6·0	− 8·3	−20·2	−12·0	+27·5	+24·2	+26·
Roskell	1411 58187	2	Original auxiliary compensation to the balance.	....	−23·9	−38·0	−42·9	−45·2	−56·2	−51·2	−11·5	− 3·8	+ 4·
				*	*	*	*	*	*	*	†	†	†
Chronometrical Thermometer...	...	..	....	+1288·7	+1539·0	+1878·0	+1959·5	+2050·0	+2499·0	+2321·0	−2288·0	−2454·0	−2553
Extremes of Temperature as shown by the Self-Registering Thermometer..........	...	..	....	38—53	34—53	33—44	30—44	30—44	22—36	22—41	70—104	75—105	80—10

* During these weeks the Chronometers were exposed to the external air outside a North window.
† During these weeks the Chronometers were placed in the chamber of a stove heated by gas.
The rate given by the first five days of trial is in every case omitted.

AT THE ROYAL OBSERVATORY, GREENWICH, 1853.

3

IN THE ORDER OF TIME.

March 9—26	Mar. 26 to April 2	April 2—9	April 9—16	April 16—23	April 23—30	April 30 to May 7	May 7—14	May 14—21	May 21—28	May 28 to June 4 †	June 4—11 †	June 11—18 †	June 18—25	June 25 to July 2	July 2—9	NAME OF MAKER.	Number.
- 2·5	+ 0·6	+ 0·7	+ 1·4	+ 2·8	+ 1·4	+ 1·0	+ 2·3	+ 3·8	+10·0	+11·4	+ 4·9	+ 6·7	+10·0	+11·8	+12·7	Lister and Son	508
-12·0	- 5·0	0·0	+ 0·9	+ 2·1	+ 1·0	+ 1·7	+ 3·3	+ 5·5	+ 5·6	- 3·1	- 2·0	- 1·0	- 1·5	+ 1·0	- 0·5	Poole	1585
- 5·6	- 1·5	- 5·9	- 6·6	- 8·1	- 5·0	-10·1	- 5·8	- 8·6	- 5·1	+ 8·2	+ 8·5	+10·0	- 2·6	- 4·9	- 0·5	Woolf	5237
- 3·0	- 1·5	- 6·0	- 3·4	- 3·3	+ 1·3	- 0·7	+ 3·2	+ 1·4	+ 1·0	- 0·5	- 3·0	- 3·5	- 7·5	- 7·0	- 7·8	Loseby..........	126
- 7·5	+ 6·5	+ 7·4	+ 5·6	+ 7·7	+ 7·4	+ 7·3	+ 6·3	+ 4·8	+ 6·3	+18·2	+25·6	+26·9	+22·0	+21·5	+18·0	Dent	2375
-22·0	- 7·8	- 0·3	- 0·2	+ 3·5	+ 0·9	+ 3·6	+ 4·0	..	..	..	..	..	..	..	..	C. Frodsham......	2484
-18·3	- 8·8	- 9·6	- 3·1	- 3·7	- 2·9	- 8·2	- 0·1	- 4·0	- 3·0	-28·5	-27·5	-23·9	- 3·4	- 1·5	- 2·9	Reid and Son	1092
- 4·2	+22·5	+24·0	+25·2	+26·8	+27·4	+26·2	+29·9	+28·0	+28·4	+19·5	+24·2	+31·4	+42·0	+45·5	+46·8	Glover..........	275
-36·5	-28·7	-26·7	-29·7	-26·7	-28·7	-25·7	-26·7	-23·0	-22·2	-38·8	-38·0	-31·0	-10·5	- 8·5	- 9·5	Hewitt and Son ...	1999
- 2·0	+ 0·5	- 8·0	+ 1·0	+11·5	- 1·0	- 8·5	- 8·0	- 6·5	+ 5·1	- 4·6	-14·5	- 4·0	+23·5	+25·0	+20·0	Dixon	380
-39·6	-34·0	-23·4	-26·7	-20·8	-25·6	-17·4	-20·0	-10·0	- 7·5	- 2·4	- 5·1	- 2·5	- 3·5	- 1·5	0·0	Lawson	1152
-19·9	-13·1	- 8·4	- 7·4	- 6·2	- 5·4	- 5·6	- 4·4	- 6·5	-11·8	+19·2	+13·6	+21·0	-12·0	- 9·5	-11·5	Eiffe	482
-65·0	-32·3	-20·0	-24·2	-20·5	-24·2	-19·3	-22·0	-15·5	-14·1	-27·9	-32·5	-27·0	-22·5	-19·5	-18·0	Hewitt	1520
-36·5	+31·8	+37·8	+35·0	+37·5	+39·8	+37·6	+51·2	+42·0	+40·8	+24·3	+19·7	+27·5	+64·5	+69·0	+81·0	M'Clellan	148
-41·2	-20·2	- 7·6	- 2·4	+ 0·5	- 3·8	- 0·7	- 0·6	+ 5·6	+ 8·0	- 4·0	-12·0	- 3·5	+24·5	+22·0	+21·0	Parkinson and Bouts	850
+ 3·3	- 2·4	- 0·5	- 1·0	+ 1·3	- 0·4	+ 1·5	+ 1·5	+ 3·5	+ 3·3	+37·9	+52·3	+49·5	+ 1·0	+ 1·5	- 0·5	Carter	535
- 3·7	-24·8	-30·0	-16·5	-20·1	-10·4	-32·2	-18·8	-47·1	-53·8	-54·4	-38·4	-52·6	- 2·9	- 1·2	-25·9	Wieland ,........	788
-18·9	+ 2·7	+16·5	+14·1	+22·9	+17·1	+24·4	+21·7	+30·3	+35·3	+32·7	+28·5	+32·1	+38·0	+45·1	+45·0	Chorley	851
-40·9	-20·8	- 6·3	- 8·2	- 3·8	- 8·6	- 1·9	- 4·6	+ 4·6	+ 6·5	+10·4 †	+11·5 †	+25·6 †	+23·7	+25·8	+33·0	Roskell	1411/58157
-2213·0	+1433·5	+747·0	+993·0	+808·5	+1142·0	+529·0	+928·5	+208·5	- 85·3	-1903·7	-3451·5	-2968·5	-116·5	-148·5	-340·7		
24—42	39—56	48—58	47—54	48—56	45—53	51—58	47—57	55—65	57—70	66—105	77—107	85—104	58—70	60—69	59—74		

The Chronometer C. Frodsham 2484 was withdrawn at the request of the Maker on May 16.

The Chronometer Wieland 788 was deposited on January 10; but its rates being so irregular as to imply some accidental cause of failure, it was taken away for examination on January 22, and returned for further trial on February 12.

The order of arrangement of the Chronometers in these Tables is determined solely by consideration of their irregularities of rate as expressed in the columns "Difference between the Greatest and Least" and "Greatest difference between one Week and the next," without reference to the duration of the Trial. The position of C. Frodsham 2484, and of Wieland 788, is therefore not necessarily correct.

26

26 *Two-Day Marine Chronometer*

by Parkinson & Frodsham, No. 3735, *c.* 1860

Although of obvious high quality this chronometer's points of interest lie in, first, the address (Change Alley); second, the fact that the crest shows that the firm claimed the Royal Appointment and third, that they commemorate the fact that they were at the Great Exhibition of 1851. Since Parkinson & Frodsham were at 4 Change Alley, Cornhill between 1851 and 1890 it means that the chronometer was made between 1852 and 1890, but since they only show the 1851 Exhibition on the dial and not the 1862 (at which they won a medal) I think it is fair to assume that the chronometer dates between 1852 and 1862. No watches in the collections of the British Museum bear this exhibition mark.

Measurements not available.

William Parkinson and W.J. Frodsham were both admitted to the Clockmakers' Company in 1802. In addition to showing in the exhibitions mentioned above they also exhibited in the Paris Exhibition of 1889.

Their other addresses were:
1891–2, 16 Queen Victoria Street,
1893–5, 35 Royal Exchange,
1896–1905, 15B Royal Exchange.

They also had business addresses in Liverpool:
1828–31, 54 Castle Street,
1831–4, 38 Castle Street.

For full details of all the Frodshams see Mercer, *The Frodshams*, 1981.

26a The box closed.

compensation is known as 'Auxiliary Compensation'. Apart from Loseby's solution, no theoretically correct solution to the problem of M.T.E. was found until the introduction by Dr C.E. Guillaume of his nickel steel and brass bimetallic balance in about 1899, known by several names but to be referred to here as the Guillaume balance. Loseby's balance is described with the chronometer that bears his name on pp. 49–51.

Before it came to the British Museum this chronometer was part of Courtenay Ilbert's collection. Ilbert acquired it from an American collector named Todhunter in 1934. It was exhibited in the 'British Watches and Clocks Exhibition' held in the City of Birmingham Museum of Science and Industry from October 1953 to February 1954.

Note: The following story told to C.A. Ilbert by A.W. Curzon in 1949 is recorded on a typed sheet together with a photograph of Schoof. These came with the chronometer when it was acquired by the British Museum. It reads as follows:

Schoof apparently made two of his five toothed 'scape wheel lever chronometers. One he left to Gardner and the other just managed to obtain a place in the Greenwich trials on an occasion when more chronometers than usual were bought. The Greenwich Schoof was stolen from 99 St. John's Street Road in about February 1889. The thief took at the same time a box of cigars, a few chronographs and Mr. A. W. Curzon's spectacles. Nothing was heard of the chronometer for approximately eight months. At that time a policeman patrolling the Mile End Road saw a known scamp carrying a parcel under his arm and stopped him, as a matter of principle, to examine it. The man stated that it was, 'Only an old clock'. Even the policeman was able to see that it was something rather more. The Police Station asked the local pawnbroker for his opinion of the value of the piece. They were told that it was worth £80, and the man further advised them to get in touch with the Horological Institute with a view to the possibility of their having some knowledge of a missing chronometer. Britten was able to identify the chronometer as Schoof's and it was returned to him. The name had been stoned off the potance plate, which in consequence was made very much thinner. As a result, the balance staff was too long and visiting cards had been placed underneath the cock to allow end shake. Schoof eventually re-finished the chronometer and sent it to Greenwich with the results that are well known. The receiver of the chronometer was sent to prison for eight years. It transpired that the chronometer would have, if it had not been recovered, been placed in a ship which was sailing the same day at 4 p.m. The receiver was in fact on his way there. No action was taken against the thief as it turned out that he was already doing penal servitude at Dartmoor. The police asked Schoof his estimation of the value of his chronometer and he said that he did not reckon that it was more than about £20. The police, however, told him that they particularly wished to prefer a substantial charge against the receiver, and Schoof, to oblige them, then stated that he valued the piece at £80.

---

31 Two-Day Marine Chronometer

by E.T. Loseby, No. 126, 1853

The usual brass-bound box is in good condition except that the ivory disc that should be inset into the top of the lid is missing and has been replaced by a blank. There is a numbered tipsy key.

The 24-hour silvered dial is inscribed *Loseby London* and within the subsidiary seconds dial, which is at the 12, is the number *126*. At 24 hours is the up-and-down subsidiary dial.

Gold spade minute and hour hands, a blued steel seconds hand. The minute hand rotates as normal, that is once an hour.

The spotted movement is of conventional full plate design. It is jewelled at the fourth on the dial side and at the escapement, this with ruby endstones except for the endstone in the balance cock which is the usual diamond. It is not generally known that the bearing faces of these diamonds is the cleavage face of the stone; this face is the hardest plane in the diamond and cannot under any circumstances be cut. Despite this fact it is possible to find cases where the face is indented by the action of the pivot upon it.

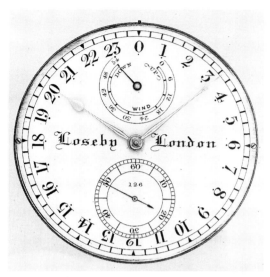

31 The dial of No. 126 which is a 24-hour dial. The up-and-down dial shows a reserve of 54 hours.

This abrading action is not really understood but a similar thing happens with diamond styli used on records, which in theory should not wear but nevertheless do.

Unusually, the fourth jewel is protected by a cap with a hole just large enough to clear the pivot. This possibly has a dual purpose, to prevent the dirt that may penetrate through the dial reaching the jewel, and secondly to protect the jewel should the extended seconds pivot be broken off.

The Earnshaw-type detent escapement has both impulse and discharge rollers jewelled and the locking stone is triangular. The balance is what makes this chronometer really interesting for it has at the ends of its two bimetal rims mercury-filled tubes which are so shaped and positioned as to not only assist in the compensation but also to eliminate Middle Temperature Error.

Loseby was not the first to use mercury in this way; in fact one of the first compensation balances to be made contained it, namely that designed by Le Roy for his famous marine timekeeper, details of which were published by him in a memoir in 1769. The remarkable chronometer described contained virtually all of the elements of a modern marine chronometer. Pierre Le Roy was born in 1717 and died in 1785, unfortunately before he could perfect his chronometers.

After Le Roy several makers attempted to make successful mercurial balances but none was able to do so, until Loseby.

Box H. 17.4 cm, 16.1 cm square.

Courtesy British Museum.

Edward Thomas Loseby

Loseby was originally apprenticed to Rotherham of Coventry and began working on his own probably about 1840; in 1851 he exhibited in the Great Exhibition. He invented his compensation balance about 1843 and in 1845 he published an article

Fig. 31a (left, centre) The movement from the back.

Fig. 31b (left, below) The balance cock removed so that the balance can be seen clearly. The timing nuts on the balance are at either end of the arm. A screw is inserted from the inside and well tightened. The nut then goes on the outside and with its splits can be arranged to be friction tight on the screw.

'Improvements in Chronometers' in the *Nautical Magazine*. In 1855 he published a pamphlet about his mercurial balance and also about improvements to mercurial pendulums. The pamphlet was entitled 'An Account of Improvements in chronometers, watches and clocks' and was published in London.

Loseby had success with his balances, gaining first place in the Greenwich trials in 1845, 1846, 1850, 1851 and 1852. In 1846 he in fact entered three chronometers and gained 1st, 2nd and 3rd places! In 1847 he only achieved 6th place and in 1849, 3rd.

Altogether the Admiralty purchased no less than thirteen of Loseby's chronometers, for which they paid a total of £630, which was in fact a higher price than they normally paid. Encouraged by his success he applied in 1852 to the Admiralty for a reward to which he felt he was entitled. However, he was met with a polite but firm refusal. Disheartened he retired from the Greenwich trials and moved from his London address (44 Gerrard Street, Islington) to Leicester where he continued as a high-class watch and clockmaker until he died in 1890. He made a remarkable turret clock for the Market Hall in Coventry which was really two clocks since the mechanism of the turret clock was controlled by an astronomical clock.

After Vulliamy died in 1854 the Lord Chamberlain asked G.B. Airy (Astronomer Royal 1835–81) to recommend someone to take over the care of the Buckingham Palace clocks. Airy said that from the point of view of personal skill alone Loseby was the ablest man. However, this honour was not to come his way and in due course Charles Fordsham was appointed (he also took over Vulliamy's business).

Despite Loseby's fame no obituary is to be found in the *H.J.* when he died.

32 *A Marine Chronometer that Strikes*

by William Shepherd, with a balance by John Hartnup, *c.* 1860

This magnificent chronometer is possibly unique in so far as it strikes. It does this at each minute, that is as the seconds hand moves from 59 to 60.

The striking can be silenced by moving a lever and was probably for checking astronomical observations. It is unlikely to have been for checking other chronometers.

The mahogany case is 7 in by 7 in by 4 in high (17.8 × 17.8 × 10 cm) with a circular aperture in the lid so as to show the glazed bezel. The lid of this outer case is fitted with catches that were almost certainly meant to hold a mirror in a recess. The lid was originally furnished with a lockable stay so that it could be fixed in any desired position so that an observer could view the chronometer whatever his or her vantage point without moving the chronometer into a vertical position which could have affected its timekeeping properties. The brass bowl with its threaded bezel fits into a recess in the wooden case.

The dial is 24 hour with the usual subsidiary dials, all the odd numerals are Arabic and the even numerals Roman (fig. 32a). The dial is engraved *WILLM. SHEPHERD, BATH ST., LIVERPOOL*. The hour and minute hands are gold and the other hands of blued steel.

The movement is a conventional chronometer except for the balance which is that designed by John Hartnup, known as the 'grid-iron'. It is seconds beating so that the seconds hand moves forwards in second steps (fig. 32b). As can be seen in fig. 32c the balance of this chronometer has inclined rims. The purpose of this is to achieve the necessary non-linear movement as already discussed. This is not the first of Hartnup's designs; to begin with the balances had plain arms, but it was found to be difficult to get enough movement with these. The type in this chronometer with bimetallic arms as well as rims was the developed form. It is fair to say that other makers of this type of balance did not achieve comparable results, as was the case with so many of these complex balances. For a full discussion of the compensated balance with many different types illustrated see *Catalogue of Watches*, Vol. 6 by Anthony Randall and Richard Good, British Museum Publications, London, 1990.

This chronometer now resides in the Merseyside County Museum.

The National Maritime Museum has a chronometer with a Hartnup balance but it is not seconds beating nor does it strike, in fact the

32

Fig. 32a

Fig. 32b

Fig. 32c

combination of the features that this chronometer has undoubtedly make it unique.

Measurements not available.

William Shepherd was a well-known Liverpool chronometer maker who had four different places of business in Liverpool between 1837 and 1853. He was in the habit of having his chronometers tested at the Liverpool Observatory. Hartnup was made Superintendant of the Liverpool Observatory when it was founded in 1844 and continued until 1855 when his place was taken by his son who was also John. Shepherd told Hartnup that he had been experimenting with balances that were intended to overcome M.T.E. but had not been successful; he further said that if Hartnup could think of a way of solving the problem then he would make up the balances. Hartnup agreed on the understanding that the results were made public.

John Hartnup was one of the first to experiment with balances with a view to eliminating Middle Temperature Error. Hartnup wrote a report for the Royal Astronomical Society which was published in Volume No. 9 p. 206, where he gave the results of his experiments showing the superiority of the balance he pioneered in conjunction with William Shepherd. The experiments took place at Greenwich in 1848; Chronometers 222, 228 and 230 were tested. Ordinarily M.T.E. was about 3 seconds a day but Hartnup reduced it to a third of this.

Middle Temperature Error (M.T.E.)

It was found that, with a steel balance spring and a plain bimetallic balance with the rims of brass and steel, it was not possible to achieve exact compensation over the desired range of temperatures. If correct compensation was achieved, say, at 4° and 36° Fahrenheit, then there would be an error midway between these temperatures of a gain of 3 seconds a day. This is known as Middle Temperature Error.

---

33 *Eight-Day Chronometer Mantel clock*

by J. Hammersley, London, *c.* 1870

The chronometer is in a brass drum case with folding bronzed feet and a handle. At the back is a

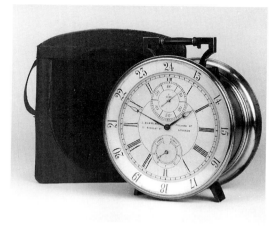

33

heavy glazed bezel with winding and hand setting shutters.

Although looking as if it has been converted from a marine chronometer the lack of a setting square on the cannon pinion shows that this is not so.

Both the dial and the bezel sight ring are silvered with the latter marked *13–24* in Arabic numerals in blue. The dial bears the name *J. Hammersley, 14, Barclay Rd. Fulham Rd. London*, also the number *1* over *2098*. The hands are all of pierced spade design. Unusually the subsidiary seconds dial is at the twelve o'clock position with the subsidiary up-and-down dial at six o'clock.

The movement has spotted plates. The fusee is reversed. A fourth wheel is a contrate wheel and the seconds hand is mounted on its arbor. The platform has a spring detent escapement. The bimetal cut balance has a helical spring of palladium, see the description of the chronometer by Thos. Mercer (on p. 54) for information on palladium springs.

Behind the chronometer the leather travelling case can be seen.

Dial 6 in (15 cm) in diameter.

John Hammersley was a clever watchmaker who specialised in the springing and adjustment of chronometers. F.J. Britten claimed that he invented the duo-in-uno balance spring but J. McLennan and J.P. Walsh contested this. Hammersley died at the age of 82 in 1901, the same year as Queen Victoria.

34 Movement of an Eight-Day Household Chronometer

by Thomas Mercer, St Albans, c. 1890

This seconds-beating movement with a platform escapement was made when Thomas Mercer was still alive; he was the founder of the firm that, four generations later, is still in existence. The bimetallic cut balance is fitted with a palladium spring, such springs were first used in the Greenwich trials in 1880 when Kullberg submitted chronometer No. 3970 and obtained second place. The following two years Riego submitted chronometers with palladium springs and after this they began to be used more and more until by the end of the century the majority of marine chronometers had such springs.

Note the winding and hand setting is from the back.

The substantial plates are finished by spotting. There is of course the usual fusee and chain with Harrison's maintaining power. All of the work in this domestic chronometer is of the same standard as it would be were it a conventional marine chronometer, the great difference being that the balance is mounted horizontally thus necessitating a contrate wheel as the fourth wheel. Although not visible, up-and-down work is fitted so as to show the state of wind.

H. 6½ in (16.5 cm).

Thomas Mercer was born in St Helens in 1822 and was a watch wheel maker until 1851 when he came to London. Shortly after his arrival he went to work for John Fletcher, chronometer maker of Lombard St., who taught him 'springing'. He eventually set up on his own in Newton St., New North Rd, having mastered the other branches of chronometer making. He next moved to Spencer St. and afterwards to 161 Goswell Rd, Clerkenwell. About 1875 he moved to St Albans where he built a factory and became the largest manufacturer of marine chronometers in the world. As stated above the firm of Thomas Mercer is still in existence, although they gave up making marine chronometers some years ago.

34

35 Eight-Day Household Chronometer

by Russell's Ltd, Liverpool, c. 1900

The thuya case with brass stringing has a glazed top with a circular spirit level inset and a hinged bezel.

A silvered dial with two subsidiary dials, one for seconds and the other for the up-and-down. The dial is inscribed *RUSSELL'S LTD. LIVERPOOL. MAKERS TO THE ADMIRALTY No. 569 8 DAY CHRONOMETER*. Between XII and I on the dial is a knob passing through a slot in the dial which is marked *STOP* at one end of the slot. This operates the balance stopping device which enables the seconds hand to be set to time.

The movement has spotted plates, a chain fusee, Harrison's maintaining power and a horizontal platform escapement. The escapement is spring detent. The bimetallic balance is free sprung with a blued steel helical spring.

H. 11½ in (29 cm).

Another and virtually identical chronometer, but bearing the name of Charles Frodsham, numbered 2364, was sold at Christie's 2 May 1979. It is highly probable that Thos Mercer made this chronometer that bears Russell's name. As evidence of this see colour plate III.

Russell was the firm *T.R. Russell* whose first address was at 22 Slater St. from 1848 to 1851. They then moved to 18 Church St., Liverpool. They were a very well-known firm with a wide range of products. They exhibited in London in 1862 and had an Honourable Mention and were still in business when Victoria died.

35

Fig. 35a One of Russell's invoices incorporating a picture of their 'Cathedral Works' at 18 Church Street. It will be seen on the right of 'Liverpool' that they state they were first established in 1745. The other point of interest is that they are on the telephone. This means that Russells were among the first to have a telephone for it was not until 1881 that the independent telephone companies joined together to form the National Telephone Co. Ltd, and only by 1890 was it possible to speak from London to the Midlands and the North and, of course, vice versa.

3 Clocks of the Cole Type

*A*t the Paris Exhibition of 1855 Thomas Cole was told by the judges that he held 'a very distinguished position for true artistic excellence and workmanship'. Thomas had a brother J.F. Cole, known as the 'English Breguet', and there is a carriage clock in the British Museum which bears both their names; this clock was made in 1823. James Ferguson Cole was an established clockmaker by the time he was twenty-two years old, and was in partnership with Thomas in Bond Street around 1823. However it would appear that Thomas desired to be on his own and is recorded as such first in Bloomsbury, at No. 11 Upper King St., this being around 1838.

Thomas married twice and we find that in 1841 his second wife was a Charlotte Boulding. They lived in Lamb's Conduit Street where their son was born a year after. By 1845 he had settled at No. 2 Upper Vernon St., in Clerkenwell and described himself as a designer and maker of ornamental clocks.

The Great Exhibition of 1851 publicised his work for the first time. He showed six pieces among which was a clock with calendar combined with an inkwell. This is shown in fig. v. Another shown by him was a portable clock of the type known as a strut clock, this was a design peculiarly his own and for ever after associated with him. Known as a strut clock for obvious reasons, examples are to be found in this chapter.

In the London Exhibition of 1862 the work of both brothers was on show. James's work was catalogued as 'new horological models' but Thomas was awarded a medal for the excellence of his taste and design. It is true to say that the movements of James's clocks were superior to those for which Thomas was responsible. However, the cases that

Thomas made were superlative and outshone those by such major makers as Vulliamy, Weeks of Coventry Street and even the best French work! Two years after the 1862 Exhibition Thomas died and his obituary is to be found in the *H.J.* for February 1864.

Some clocks bear Thomas's name on the dial, but mainly these clocks were made for others, for example, Payne of 165 New Bond Street, C.F. Hancock who, during this period, was at 19 Bruton Street and 152 Bond Street, Hunt & Roskell, and Howell & James. Sometimes the clocks bear the name of the vendor only, sometimes there is a signature hidden away on the movement, sometimes there is no signature of any sort to be

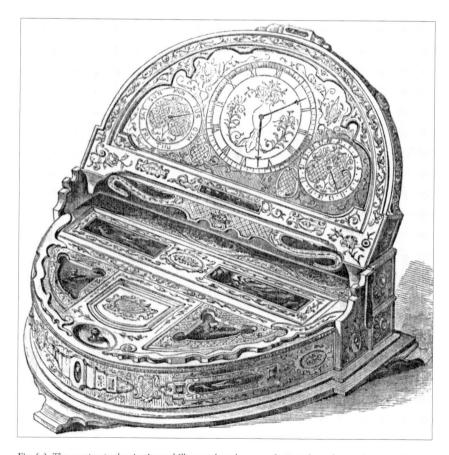

Fig. (v) The caption in the *Art-Journal Illustrated* catalogue reads, 'An inkstand, or to designate it more correctly according to its varied contents, a compendium for the writing-table, made and contributed by Mr. COLE, of Clerkenwell, is a most useful and elegant work of manufacturing art; novel in character when the variety and arrangement of its "fittings" is considered, and most elaborately engraved and richly ornamented.'

found. A technical criticism of these otherwise admirable clocks lies in their platform escapements which are not of a quality consistent with that of the rest of the clock. What makes the problem worse is that they are so often mounted vertically.

The superb cases are built up on a central casting, always flawless, the applied mounts being also cast. The mounts are built up in layers, these being pierced and engraved. The engraving is often in relief contrasting and alternating with the normal type of engraving. An unexpected feature of the dials of these clocks is that the numerals are often painted, surprising when so much other engraving was being done. The hands of Cole's clocks are almost always of the fleur-de-lis design.

From about 1846 the clocks were numbered in sequence, starting at 500 and ending at 1900 in 1864; it is probable that 200 clocks had been made before he began this sequence. There was also an ancillary number associated with the type of clock. The oval 30-hour clock was given the number 202. Together with his rectangular strut clock, these were his most popular styles and were the backbone of his trade. All the different types he made will not be discussed here as they will appear subsequently.

Cole was nothing if not versatile, as is evidenced by the clock bearing the name Barry. This has a beautiful blue porcelain dial probably by Minton with flowers and two figures in a garden.

There is a specialist book, *Thomas Cole and Victorian Clockmaking*, written by John Hawkins. To launch the book in England there was an exhibition of Thomas Cole's work held at the premises of Algernon Asprey in Bruton Street. It was held in November 1975. Sixty-nine clocks were displayed each of which are described and discussed in the book with the exception of six late additions to the exhibition. These latter clocks were lent by the late Lord Harris.

Clocks in the Cole style continued to be made into the twentieth century. Three such clocks are shown in Hawkins' book, two of them being made by E. White, an example of whose work is to be found elsewhere in this volume, on p. 110.

36 Desk Clock

in the manner of Thomas Cole, signed
Hunt & Roskell, London, No. 15599,
c. 1850

The gilt metal case is copiously engraved, the
base is set with a thermometer.

The silvered dial is florally engraved on a matt
ground. The minute hand is plain, the hour hand
is of Gothic design, they are blued steel.

The movement has a lever escapement with a
plain balance and strikes on a wire gong.

H. 13¾ in (35 cm).

Hunt & Roskell of Manchester and London, 1843–1965

The firm of Hunt & Roskell came into being in 1843
although before this there were two Hunts in the firm
of Mortimer & Hunt. Upon Mortimer's retirement in
1843 the partners were J.S. Hunt, J. Hunt, Robert
Roskell junior and Charles Frederick Hancock. Hancock
had his own business at 3 St Anne's Square and retired
from Hunt & Roskell in 1849, however he shared the

manufactory with Hunt & Roskell at 26, Harrison
Street.

Hunt & Roskell's shop 1844–1911 was at 156 New
Bond Street. They employed no less than thirty-five
people at the retail premises and about a hundred at the
manufactory. They were silversmiths and jewellers to
the Queen. J.S. Hunt died in 1865 leaving a staggering
£120,000. John Hunt died in 1879 aged 68. Hunt &
Roskell continued in business at the same address with
R. Roskell, Allan Roskell and John Mortimer Hunt until
the death of R. Roskell in 1888. This was the finish of
the firm for the two remaining partners and they sold
out to J.W. Benson in 1889. By 1897 the firm had
become Hunt & Roskell Ltd.

A visitor to the retail premises in 1865 described a
single diamond there as the finest stone on display in
Europe valued at about £8,000. A bracelet was
described formed of diamonds surrounding two ovals
for miniatures which instead of having glass to protect
them had diamond panes. Thus there is nothing new
abut the crystal 'glasses' that we find in today's wrist
watches, which actually turn out to be a bit down-
market by comparison! Although no mention is made
about clocks we know of course that they dealt in them
since they showed clocks at the Great Exhibition of
1851 and also at the International Exhibition of 1862
when they received an Honourable Mention.

37 Tripod Clock

(Thomas Cole, London), No. 1782/62,
c. 1860

The tripod that supports the movement and the
pendulum, stands on a moulded circular base, the
top of which is engraved with arabesque foliage
within strapwork. The base has three levelling
feet and is set with a thermometer, an aneroid
barometer and a beat scale which can be raised to
lock the pendulum.

The concave silvered dial is similarly engraved
to the base and has a quatrefoil layout. There is a
sunk subsidiary seconds dial. The numerals are
painted.

The blued steel moon hands neither match nor
are original, the seconds hand is however original.

The winding square, by virtue of offset
winding, has been brought below the dial.

36

The pendulum is supported from the top of the tripod and has a spherical bob. Above the pendulum suspension is a plumb bob.

There is a clear view of the movement in fig. 37a, it is arranged in two tiers with the slower moving parts below. It is a going barrel movement with a dead beat escapement.

H. 20½ in (52 cm).

38 *Tripod Timepiece Month Going*

in the manner of Cole

Similar to the preceding clock, but this illustration gives a very clear view of the base.

Measurements not available.

Above **37**; below **Fig. 37a**

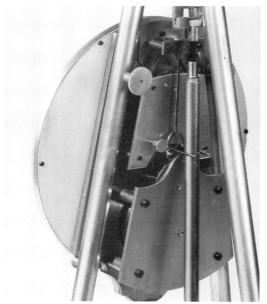

38

39 *Strut Desk Clock*

in the manner of Cole, *c.* 1845

The gilt brass rectangular case is of the strut type with a turnbuckle foot and a carrying handle at the top.

The dial is engraved with scrolling foliage outside of the chapter ring with arabesques within. Beneath the dial is a type of perpetual calendar (explained below).

The hands are not original, they should no doubt be fleur-de-lis. The numerals are painted.

The 8-day movement has a vertically mounted platform with a lever escapement and a plain balance.

This clock is almost identical in form to Item 1 p. 46, signed *Hunt & Roskell 162 New Bond Street* in Hawkins' book on Cole. See the Bibliography.

The calendar is unusual in that it is a form of perpetual calendar. The rolling day indicator has seven facets with each commencing at the top with successive days of the week.

There are rules that can be followed to enable this rolling day indicator to be reset so that the day of the week is correct as each new month arrives but these rules are really quite complicated. The easiest way to set it correctly is just to check with a calendar or one's diary. The day roller is advanced by means of a key which is inserted through a hole in base of the clock.

Measurements not available.

40 *Timepiece*

by Hunt & Roskell, *c.* 1855

A gilt-metal case with easel support and small ring handle; the border decorated with leafy scrolls and flowers. Silvered dial engraved with strapwork, leaves and flowers, signed *Hunt & Roskell London* and fleur-de-lis hour hand and plain minute hand (not unusual in Cole clocks). The clock has a manually adjusted calendar. Movement with lever escapement bearing *Thos. Cole* secret signature.

H. 5 in (12.7 cm).

For a similar but more elaborate clock (but with a different type of strut) see Hawkins, p. 72, item 13.

39

40

41 Desk Clock

by William Taylor, London, *c.* 1855

The case is of a layered construction, the various parts being cast. The outset corners of the base are set with miniature pinnacles (one is missing in the photograph).

The whole case is engraved with foliage and flowers on a hatched ground.

The silvered dial has an engraved centre and painted Gothic numerals. It is inscribed *Will Taylor 15 Spencer St Clerkenwell.*

The dial has a florally pierced and engraved mask of the same design as the carriage clock by Arnold/Chas. Frodsham in the Carriage Clocks chapter, no. 4.

The movement is going barrel with a platform with a lever escapement.

Striking is on a gong, the block that supports this gong is stamped *J.P.*

H. 6¾ in (17 cm).

William Taylor is known to have been at 15 Spencer Street, Goswell Road, Clerkenwell from 1853 to 1858.

41

42 A Strut Timepiece with a Porcelain Dial

made by Thomas Cole for James Barry, London, *c.* 1860
See colour plate IV

This strut-type case is picture-like in its presentation with the 'frame' engraved and with a small mask to the porcelain dial. The dial is probably by Minton and has a rich sky blue background. The gilt chapter ring is skeletonised with foliage surrounding each Roman numeral.

Within the chapter ring is a delicate floral circlet. Beneath the dial in a cartouche formed of gilt scrolling foliage is a painted scene of a couple in a garden.

The movement is stamped *Thos Cole London and Barry.* It has a platform with a lever escapement and a plain balance.

H. 8½ in (20.5 cm). W. 5½ in (14 cm).

For a similar clock see Hawkins, p. 87.

James Barry was at 3 Belmont Terrace, Wandsworth Rd., from 1858 to 1864 and at 181 Upper Kennington Lane from 1871 to 1875.

43 Strut Clock of the Cole Type

by Howell & James & Co., London, *c.* 1900

A richly gilded, chased, pierced and engraved case. The dial mask also finished similarly. The dial with Gothic numerals and fleur-de-lis hands of blued steel. Note also the fleur-de-lis in the pierced feet. A clock of superb quality, possibly made for royalty.

The movement is of better quality than one usually associated with these Cole-type clocks for the platform with its lever escapement has a temperature compensated bimetallic balance. Unfortunately the platform is still mounted vertically, not a good idea if the aim is accuracy in timekeeping.

H. 10½ in (27 cm).

For a similar high-quality clock see Hawkins, p. 76.

Howell & James

The chronology of the firm is as follows:

Howell & James 1819 to *c.* 1838
Howell & James & Co., *c.* 1838–84
Howell & james Ltd., 1884–1911

The original proprietors of this firm were John Howell and Isaac James but when the style of the firm was changed in about 1838 the partners were J. Howell, Henry Gillett, Thomas Stroud and William Sedgwick.

The firm began life as silk mercers and retail jewellers and dealt in clocks certainly by the time of the Great Exhibition, since they showed 'a large Or-molu clock representing Jupiter, the twelve Hours of the Sun, Apollo and Diana, Spring and Autumn strewing flowers and fruit of the earth with another similar, both modelled and designed by G.G. Adams, Esq.'

At the close of 1860 they opened new rooms at Regent Street and then exhibited again in the International Exhibition of 1862 where they once more showed clocks among a variety of other objects. In 1865 when Howell & James were at the peak of their success they were visited by a Henry Mayhew who reported the following:

The ceiling of the more recent parts of the buildings is lofty, and arranged in the best style of modern shop-building; the carpeted floor soft to the tread and pleasing to the eye; and around the room are arranged time-pieces of every variety and design, and counters glazed like ferneries, but containing white velvet cases in which repose jewels of every kind and value.

He went on to describe the ormolu clocks including some in the Mediaeval style enriched with coloured enamels for which the designs by a student of the South Kensington Museum were on view; every variety of inkstand in ormolu, 'the more *bizarre* the design the better, we are told, it takes with the public,' including some in the form of horses' hooves, carts and hat-boxes, and *carte-de-visite* albums set with Wedgwood intaglios. Upstairs Mayhew went on to inspect more sober clocks, one of which in enamelled terracotta was to be submitted to the Charing Cross Hotel Co (he noted in passing that Howell, James & Co had supplied all the clocks for the Grosvenor Hotel).

He also reported that there was a staff of over a hundred and that forty young women lived over the premises in Regent Street, many of whom had separate bedrooms. He also said that there was not a pallid face to be seen among them.

Their success continued and they showed at both the Paris Exhibition in 1867 and in London in 1872.

Their premises were reconstructed in 1881 with a new terracotta façade – this was to underline their interest in the new art movement. Among the clocks they stocked was a tile-mounted mantel clock designed by Lewis F. Day and a Linthorpe pottery combined clockcase and flask. This latter was designed by Christopher Dresser and was sold at Sothebys in 1972, 9 November lot 35 and in 1981, 10 December lot 185.

44 *A Chiming Mantel Clock with a Case*

probably by Thomas Cole, but Anonymous, No. 1796, *c.* 1860

The domed case is of coromandel wood and gilt-metal veneered in strongly figured wood and with ebony mouldings; surmounted by a sphinx on a beaded plinth. There are side frets over glass formed as Moorish arches enclosing vases of flowers below crossed palms trees. The corners are set with winged male figures, semi-nude, each holding two torches. The base has outset corners.

An arched silvered dial, arabesque engraved divided into quarters with a surround of diamond

43

44

45

lattice, below this is a hand set calendar of the same type as that described before.

The twin chain-fusee movement has maintaining power and a platform with a lever escapement. It chimes the quarters on four bells and strikes the hours on a gong. The back plate is numbered 1796 and carries a strike/silent lever.

H. 17 in (43 cm).

A clock with a very similar case is described and illustrated in Hawkins 1975, pp. 98 and 99.

The style of this clock is a reversion to earlier styles of the 1830s/1840s.

45 *Strut Timepiece*

in the manner of Thomas Cole, but Anonymous

Multi-piece gilded case of square form fully engraved with a folding strut and a ring at top.

Engraved silvered dial with blue steel fleur-de-lis hands, going barrel movement with vertical lever escapement and a cut compensated balance.

H. 5½ (14 cm).

46–8 *A Group of three Clocks all in English Cases*

From left to right.

46 *A Gilt-Metal Strut Timepiece*

in the manner of Cole but signed
W. Barker, London, *c.* 1880

A gilt-metal case with a break-arch top, the dial flanked by fluted pilasters. The whole of the outside of the case shaped.

A silvered dial with an engraved foliate surround. Blued steel fleur-de-lis hands.

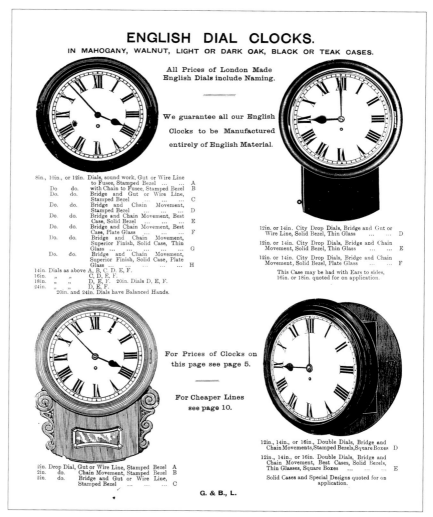

Fig. (vi) A page from Grimshaw and Baxter's catalogue. The prices of the clocks are shown in fig. (vii) overleaf.

cupboard within the gallery structure. There is a gallery clock in the British Museum building although it is actually in a part which until the British Library moves is used by them. Made by Dent it has a seconds pendulum.

Although this Dent clock is weight driven the movement of the English dial clock is usually spring driven with a fusee and pendulum. The plates are of good solid brass, the escapement usually anchor, although higher quality versions might have a dead-beat escapement.

PRICES OF ENGLISH DIAL CLOCKS, Etc.

All Prices of English Dials include Naming.

Illustrations on PAGE 4.	Quality	A	B	C	D	E	F	G	H
Round Dials, 8in., 10in., and 12in. ...		55/-	65/-	69/-	73/-	81/-	92/-	106/-	117/-
,, 14in.		72/-	82/-	87/-	97/-	102/-	114/-	—	—
,, 16in.		—	—	126/-	136/-	150/-	169/-	—	—
,, 18in.		—	—	—	175/-	195/-	220/-	—	—
,, 20in.		—	—	—	220/-	245/-	275/-	—	—
,, 24in.		—	—	—	315/-	345/-	385/-	—	—
Drop Dials, shew Pendulum, 12in.		65/-	75/-	79/-	83/-	—	—	—	—
City Drop Dials, 12in.		—	—	—	85/-	93/-	103/-	--	—
,, ,, ,, 14in.		—	—	--	110/-	120/-	140/-	—	—

Ears to City Drop Cases, extra 6/-.

Round Double Dials, 12in.		—	—	—	135/-	151/-	—	—	—
,, ,, 14in.		—	—	—	165/-	197/-	—	--	—
,, ,, 16in.		—	—	—	220/-	260/-	—	—	—

Black Cases extra. Round from 3/- each. Drop, 5/- each.

Oak or Walnut Cases 1/- extra for 8in., 10in., 12in., and 14in., Round Dials, and 12in. shew Pendulum, Drop Dials, qualities A, B, C, and D.

Teak Cases extra. Round from 4/- each. Drop, 6/- each. Double from 8/- each.

Dials to Wind and Set at Back, and any Special Design or size quoted for on application.

We guarantee all our English Clocks to be Manufactured entirely of English Material.

Fig. (vii) See fig. (vi)

The dial at this period was usually of painted iron, convex at the start of our period and flat as the century progresses. Both convex and flat glasses were used up until about 1880 when flat glasses predominated. Hands were, at the start of our period, spade – both the hour and the minute having the spade tip – but this gradually disappeared from the minute hand as the century progressed.

Bezels changed also, starting off as cast complete with sight ring but by the 1860s were spun from thin sheet first without and then with sight rings. Both types had a plastered-in glass. As to the case styles it is perhaps best to describe these as we come to the examples illustrated.

52 Views of a typical English Dial Clock Movement, Weight Driven

The pendulum is not shown, it is perfectly ordinary and uncompensated.

Measurements not available.

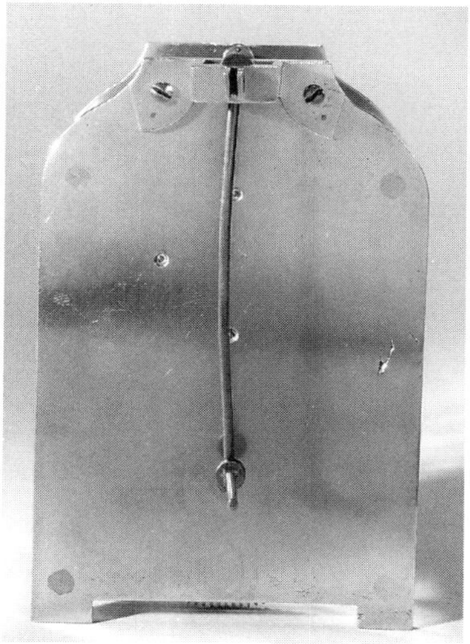

Fig. 52c The movement from the side.

Fig. 52a This shows the movement from the back, the crutch and the back cock are in full view.

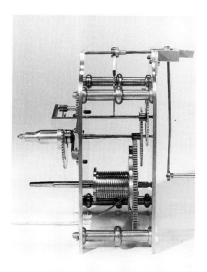

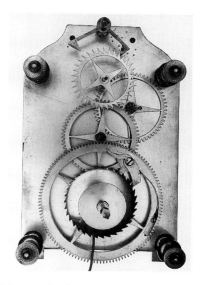

Fig. 52b Visible here is the under dial work. Below the motion work is the winding square.

Fig. 52d Between the plates looking from the front. At the top is a good view of the anchor escapement.

53–8

53–8 *A Group of Six English Dial Timepieces*

From left to right above and below.

53 *A Brass Inlaid Mahogany Drop Dial Timepiece*

by Morgan & Adehison, Bristol, *c.* 1870

The painted convex dial is inscribed *Morgan and Adehison No. 14 & 23 Union Street, Bristol*. The hands are of brass and of spade design. The iron false plate for the dial is marked *Walker & Hughes Birmingham*.

The movement has a gut fusee, shaped plates and an anchor escapement.

H. 27½ in (70 cm).

54 *A plain Mahogany Drop Dial Timepiece*

by Dutton, Fleet St., London, 1852

The silvered dial has engraved Roman numerals and the Royal Cypher, dated 1852. The hands are of blued steel and of spade design. There is a gut fusee and anchor escapement to the movement.

H. 18 in (46 cm).

55 *A Mahogany Passing Strike Drop Dial Timepiece with Calendar*

by Garland, Plymouth, *c.* 1870

The case is decorated with brass inlay and is flanked by carved ears. There are side fish-scale frets.

A painted convex dial, with a calendar dial below the XII. Above the VI is the signature, *Garland Plymouth*. The hands are brass and of spade design. The calendar hand is blued steel.

A gut-fusee movement with shaped plates and with passing strike on a bell, an unusual addition to an English dial clock.

Measurements not available.

56, 57 These next two clocks are too early for this book being about 1800.

58 *An Octagonal Rosewood English Dial Timepiece*

signature unreadable, but the place Bath still legible, *c.* 1840

The case is inlaid with brass all around the outside of the bezel.

A painted dial with the signature so faded and rubbed as to be indecypherable. The hands of spade design and of blued steel. The movement with a gut fusee and shaped plates.

The case is 17 in (43 cm) across.

59

60

59–60 *A Group of Two English Dial Clocks*

59 A mahogany-cased, drop dial timepiece by Seal of Bristol with carved ear pieces to the trunk, and an arc-shaped window to show the pendulum bob. The bottom door can be seen partly open.

Unusual hands, basically of spade design but with a trefoil just before the spade end of each hand. A brass sight ring around the glass, and brass stringing. This clock was probably made about 1870.

60 The second clock, which is anonymous, is very much like the previous clock but the shape of the window is different. The hands indicate a late clock, probably 1890. Note how plain the ear pieces are on this clock, they are most unobtrusive.

Measurements not available.

61 *English Dial Striking Clock*

by E. Baker of Birmingham, *c.* 1860

Another example of the more unusual striking clock in a fine drop dial case with an octagonal surround to the bezel. This and the whole of the front of the case, which is mahogany, is inlaid with mother-of-pearl and pewter.

The trunk below the dial has a glazed aperture through which the pendulum bob is visible. The rounded bottom has a door set into it, this is, of course, in addition to the side doors and enables regulation to be done.

A good clear dial rather spoilt by a lack of finesse in the application of the signature which is composed of a motley collection of styles of lettering. The hands are of a stylised fleur-de-lis design.

Measurements not available.

61

62 *English Dial Striking Clock*

by Austin & Hall, *c.* 1880

A drop dial case with a carved mahogany surround to the bezel. The front of the case below the dial is veneered with well-figured mahogany and there are ear pieces on either side. These ear pieces often get knocked off but traces can usually be found showing that they were originally there. The trunk terminates in a heavy moulding.

The dial is very clear, with medium-weight Roman numerals. The hands are of brass with a spade hour hand and a plain minute hand.

The twin winding squares show that this is one of the more unusual types of English dial in that it strikes; English dials are usually timepieces. The access doors to this movement can only be at the side of the trunk.

Measurements not available.

62

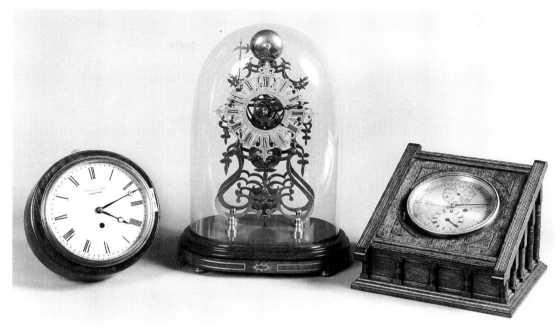

63–5 *A Group of Three Clocks*

63 On the left is a small English dial timepiece. It is in a plain mahogany case and has a painted dial bearing the name *George Douglas DUMBARTON* (known to have been at Holytown, Dumbarton in 1847). The hands are blued steel moon pattern.

The movement has a fusee with Harrison's maintaining power and a platform with a ratchet tooth lever escapement.

W. 7 in (17.8 cm).

64 The skeleton clock in the centre of the photograph is a 'one at the hour' striking timepiece. These passing strike clocks have a cam on the centre arbor which slowly raises the hammer allowing it to fall when the hand reaches the XII.

There is a chain-fusee and an anchor-recoil escapement. The plain and uncompensated pendulum beats half-seconds.

H. 12 in (30.5 cm).

65 On the right is a marine chronometer which has been mounted on a slant in a sort of table lecturn made of oak. On the dial of the chronometer is engraved the statement *Greenwich Time.* When this was first engraved it is possible that it was no more than an indication of its accuracy but after 1916 it would have had an additional meaning since 'Daylight Saving' was introduced in that year. This was the brainchild of a true Victorian, a Mr William Willett who was born in 1857.

It would therefore have been incumbent upon the owner of this chronometer not to alter the hands when Summertime arrived or departed. In 1941 Double Summer Time was introduced so that at certain times of the year this chronometer, had the owner a regard for the truth, would have shown a two-hour difference between the time shown by it and the rest of the clocks in the house.

Measurements not available.

70 *'Big Ben' Long-Case Clock*
by Jonne Salvam, *c.* 1890

The case is of carved oak. The dial has a gilt-metal pierced overlay to simulate the illuminated dial of the real 'Big Ben'.

The chiming movement has three trains and is of massive construction. There are eight tubular chimes for the Westminster chimes (tubular chimes were first patented by Harrington in 1885 and this must of necessity put this clock between 1885 and 1901) and another tubular chime for the hour strike. Not quite a replica of Big Ben for this long-case clock has a dial on the front only. It bears the inscription *Made by Jonne Salvam in the reign of Queen Victoria.*

Note the form of the '4' on the dial which is IV, the Gothic form as it is on the full-size Big Ben, seldom noticed by anybody despite the fact that this is the best-known clock in the world. In the vast majority of examples the 4 is written IIII, this leads to the question, Why is this so when it is usually written IV? The truth is that the 4 strokes were the common form in antiquity, only in recent centuries has the other form become usual. Furthermore the 4 strokes give a better appearance to the dial since they balance the heavy VIII on the other side of the dial.

H. 10 ft (305 cm).

Clocks of this type were produced for many years. In the 1890s they retailed for 100 guineas. They were still appearing in the 1906 catalogue of S. Smith & Sons and were recorded as being 10½ ft (320 cm) high, 2 ft (61 cm) wide and 1 ft 5 in (43 cm) deep, weighing nearly 5 cwt (254 kg)! Smiths said that the case alone took three months to make. They also claimed that it kept time to about a second a week!

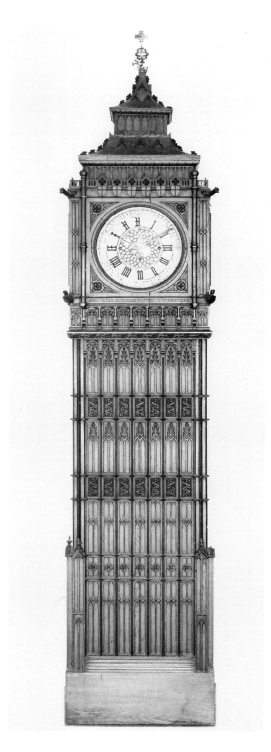

70

71 *Long-Case Clock with Quarter Chiming*

by Jay R. Attenborough & Co. Ltd,
London, *c.* 1890

The hood of the case has swan-neck cresting with a ball finial at its centre. The break-arched door to the hood is flanked by turned pillars with a carved centre divider and leaf-carved capitals. The trunk of the case has a glazed door and is also flanked by turned pillars with a centre divider, both this and the capitals are turned. The plinth has a patterned panel.

There is a break-arch dial with a subsidiary seconds dial and in the arch a second subsidiary dial with chime/silent. Within the silvered chapter ring is the inscription *Jay R. Attenborough & Co. Ltd. 142 & 144 Oxford St.*

The three-train weight-driven movement chimes on four tubular gongs and strikes on a blued steel spiral gong. Although the clock has a dead-beat escapement the pendulum is uncompensated.

H. 8 ft 11 in (272 cm).

71

72 Long-Case Chiming Clock, Chinese Chippendale style

by Thomas Turner, London, last quarter of the nineteenth century

The case is finely carved with a scale mounted pediment surmounted by figures of Oriental musicians. There are outset moulded columns flanking the blind fret carved hood door above a serpentine moulded canopy. The hood has fretted sides. There are outset columns to the main door and sides which have glazed-in fretting. There is blind fretting around the door. The columns are supported by warrior figures. The plinth has carved panels and terms on a foliate moulded base which has massive hairy claw feet. A truly impressive piece of work.

A break-arch painted dial, 14 in (36 cm) wide with lunar work in the arch. Two subsidiary dials one for the seconds and the other for the date. Within the chapter ring are the controls for four/eight bells and chime/silent selection and the signature *Turner London*.

The massive movement has an anchor escapement (fig. 72a). It chimes on nine rod gongs. The pendulum bob and the three weights are brass cased.

H. 9 ft 10 in (300 cm).

Right **72**; above **Fig. 72a**

Fig. 73a This view of one of J.W. Benson's workshops in the 'Steam Factory 62 & 64, Ludgate Hill' shows a large and airy room and the machinery driven by overhead belting. Right at the back of the room is the steam engine that powers the shafting; this runs continuously and the lathes are usually brought into action by shifting the belt from an idle pulley onto a continuously driven pulley. The shop that we see is obviously devoted to making turret clocks. On the mezzanine floor above men are sitting and these are no doubt the watchmakers. In the room on the right we see a regulator and watches hanging up on test. Unfortunately the dial clock in the main workshop and that in the room on the right do not agree. The man on the left coming down the spiral staircase seems to be carrying a box chronometer.
This is part of a Benson advertisement published in the *London Illustrated News* on 13 December 1884. At the bottom of the full page it says 'J.W. Benson Watchmaker to the Queen.' and another address is also given; 'West End House 25, Old Bond Street, London'.

73   *Long-Case Chiming Clock*

by J.W. Benson, London, 1872–3

The mahogany case is liberally applied with ormulu mounts. The hood has a shallow dome top with a broad leaf finial on either side. The door has, most unusually, an ormulu egg-and-leaf border and is flanked by triple cluster columns with acanthus capitals and corbel bases. The base of the clock has a shaped panel and again is flanked by acanthus-carved cluster corbels.

The dial is 13¾ in (34.8 cm) square with four subsidiary dials at the corners as follows: chime/silent; bell or gong chiming; calendar; and day of the week. Also, a subsidiary seconds dial is situated below the XII o'clock. Just above the VI is the signature *J.W. Benson, 25 Old Bond St., London*. The blued steel hands are of a fancy trident form.

The weight-driven chiming mechanism has three trains and massive plates, the back plate is signed as is the dial. The clock has a seconds pendulum.

The chime, as indicated on the dial, can be on either bells or gongs, a most unusual feature.

A most imposing piece, although obviously not to everyone's taste.

H. 7 ft 11 in (241 cm).

73

J.W. Benson were in business from 1844 to 1973. They traded as J.W. Benson from 1856 to 1891 after which they became a limited liability company. They held Royal warrants during the 19th century and had an honourable mention in the 1862 Exhibition. Since they were only in Bond Street from 1872 to 1873 this clock can be dated exactly.

Note: By the end of Queen Victoria's reign there were several different chiming versions available, what was chosen being governed by taste and/or the depth of the pocket of the purchaser. At the cheaper end was the fixed chiming barrel and the 5-rod set of gongs giving Westminster chimes only. The next step up would be 7 rods and a sliding barrel giving either Westminster or Whittington chimes, or an even classier version with 9 rods giving Westminster, Whittington and St Michael chimes. The really ornate clocks such as those made by Rowley (see p. 12) would have both bells and gongs fitted. Often the gongs would be for the Westminster chime and the hour strike, with the bells reserved for the lighter St Michael and Whittington chimes.

74 Quarter-Chiming Long-Case Clock with one weight and two mainsprings for the mechanism

by John Moore & Sons, Clerkenwell, c. 1870

A most unusual clock with a figured mahogany case with an arch top and a glazed front. There are carved and pierced leaf mouldings beneath the dial. The large panelled plinth has a further base with moulded rectangular feet. On either side of the case, level with the movement, the side walls are fretted to let out the sound.

The round dial has a subsidiary seconds dial. On an arc below the XII and I is *JOHN MOORE & SONS CLERKENWELL LONDON 14497*, this is also repeated on the movement back plate.

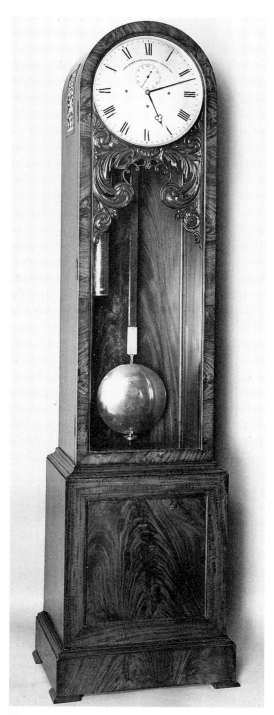

Fig. 74a

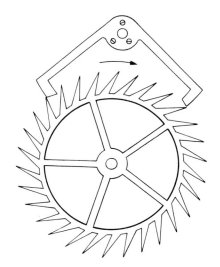

Fig. 74b

74

On the left can be seen the single driving weight which powers the going train, for although the striking and chiming trains are spring driven this was not considered satisfactory for the going train of a precision clock. The pendulum is a wood rod/lead bob combination.

Fig. 74a shows the mechanism and the chiming train with its chain fusee on the left. As can be seen the chiming is on eight bells with the striking on a single bell on the right.

The clock has a dead-beat escapement (fig. 74b). The going train is in the centre of the movement so that the weight cord is taken off to the side below the level of the seat board; note the massive size of the seat board. Again, as is so often the case with these precision clocks, the pendulum hangs from the backboard.

Measurements not available.

John Moore & Sons

John Moore was originally in partnership with Handley as Handley & Moore but set up on his own in 1824 at 38 Clerkenwell Close where the firm was to stay. In 1849 Benjamin R. & J. Moore published a pattern book *Designs for Clocks*.

John Moore exhibited in the Great Exhibitions of 1851 and 1862, in the latter exhibition he obtained a medal. By 1877 the firm is recorded as having made 15,180 house clocks. The last of the clockmaking Moores, Henry James died in 1899 aged sixty but the firm carried on in business into the twentieth century.

The wood rod and lead bob combination

An idea seems to be prevalent that the wood rod and lead bob combination does not give a 'proper' compensated pendulum. This is not true for the results can be good providing the wood of the rod is well protected against the effects of changes in its moisture content, and providing also that it is made from a piece of straight-grained well-seasoned timber. A good choice for the wood is yellow pine and it should be protected from moisture either by varnish or by gilding. The lead bob that should go with such a rod would need to be about a seventh of the length of the rod in diameter. The trouble with this type of pendulum is that it is not likely to give good long-term results. Neither wood nor lead are sufficiently stable materials for this to be likely. Nevertheless thousands of these pendulums are still in use and are giving perfectly acceptable results.

This combination can be improved by substituting zinc for the lead, since they have more or less the same coefficient of expansion.

Ferdinand Berthoud conducted experiments on wood rod pendulums which resulted in him damning them completely but it is not even clear if he varnished the rods.

There are rumours that both teak and ebony have zero coefficients of expansion over the normal range of temperatures but I have not checked on this nor do I know of any one else who has. Common sense tells me that it is not true. Certainly Vulliamy used centre supported bobs with ebony rods but this does not necessarily prove anything since they were not intended to be precision clocks.

Although it might seem natural for this type of pendulum to have been the first to have been invented this is not so. This was left to those giants of horology, George Graham and John Harrison. Graham invented the mercurial pendulum in about 1725 and Harrison the grid-iron in about 1729. Both were in frequent use during the Victorian era.

75 *Wall Clock*

by J. & A. Jump, London, No. 138, *c.* 1870

The case is mahogany and has a hood with a carved foliate bezel, an arched glazed door and a concave moulded base. The 12 in (30 cm) silvered circular dial is inscribed *J. & A. Jump London No. 138*.

The movement has a dead-beat escapement and Harrison's maintaining power. The pendulum is of the wood rod/lead bob type and as with many regulators the weight is taken off to the side to keep it away from the pendulum. However this example cannot be classed as a regulator since it has no seconds hand.

H. 5 ft 2 in (157 cm).

For details of J. and A. Jump see the carriage clock section, p. 28.

75

76 *Striking Long-Case Clock*

by Edward Samm, Linton, *c.* 1850

A mahogany case, the hood has a break-arch door flanked by turned pillars with a horned pediment. The trunk is fitted with a break-arch door with fluted canted corners above a panelled plinth. The case is inlaid throughout with chequer stringing and satinwood fan medallions.

The 12 in (30 cm) wide break-arch dial has a silvered chapter ring and a matted centre. On an arc on the centre is inscribed *Edward Samm Linton*. Unusual spandrels take the form of the four seasons. In the arch the moon dial is showing the very start of the waxing cycle. The blued steel hands are of serpentine form. All in all an elegant clock.

The striking movement has an anchor escapement and an uncompensated pendulum.

H. 7 ft 8 in (234 cm).

76

77 *Long-Case Striking Clock with Lunar and Date Work*

made by S. Kellet of Bradbury,
mid-nineteenth century

A finely figured mahogany case of large proportions typical of country clocks of this period and a very good example of its kind.

The broken-arch hood has a swan-neck pediment but the pediment is now broken; the hood has three finials. The door is flanked by fluted columns.

The whole case is inlaid with stringing and various motifs. A panel in the bottom of the door and the panelled plinth both have inlaid fan patera in each corner of their panels. The door in the trunk has a Gothic top and is flanked on either side by fluted columns similar to those on the hood. The plinth panel is also flanked by fluted decoration. The plinth has ogee bracket feet.

The break-arch painted dial has, at its centre, birds and flowers with girls depicting the seasons in the corners. Above the dial in the arch are more female figures, as there are between the two moons in the arch. The moons are so positioned that they are not visible in the photograph. Around the edge of the moon dial is marked the age of the moon. Within the chapters is the date ring. The date hand is blued steel, the main hands are brass.

The movement has a recoil escapement with an uncompensated pendulum. It strikes the hours and the half-hours on a bell.

H. 8 ft 1 in (246 cm).

77

PUBLIC
RECORD
OFFICE

N°2 .D 1843.

78

Fig. 78a

78 Three-Month watchman's Clock No. 2

by Vulliamy, London, 1843

The clock has a very plain mahogany case. It has a fixed 24-hour chapter ring, the night hours being in black and the day hours in red. Within this fixed ring is a rotating 24-hour dial marked in quarters, hours and with 96 pins around its periphery. (see fig. 78a) There is a single minute hand recording against the outer minute circle on the fixed dial. The hours are shown by the inner dial against a pointer at the top XII o'clock. Winding is at the bottom XII o'clock.

The dial is inscribed *VULLIAMY LONDON* with the government mark in the top left-hand corner and *PUBLIC RECORD OFFICE.* in the top right-hand corner, *No. 2* bottom left and *A.D. 1843.* bottom right.

On operating the pull on the right-hand side of the top of the trunk the watchman pushed in a pin thus revealing the fact that he was at the clock at whatever times the pins are depressed. The next day the foreman or somebody in authority can note the frequency and times of the visits and having a case key can reset the pins.

H. 6 ft 9 in.

Courtesy British Museum.

Benjamin Lewis Vulliamy was born in 1780 and died in 1854. He was made free of the Clockmakers' Company in 1809 and was Master of the Company no less than five times, in 1821, 1823, 1825, 1827 and 1847. Up until the time of his death he was in charge of the clocks in Buckingham Palace and was Clockmaker to no less than three sovereigns, George IV, William IV and Victoria. He was noted for the exactness and excellent finish of his work, examples are to be found in many palaces especially Windsor.

Vulliamy's business was based at 68 Pall Mall and he used to send an assistant on horseback or by river on a six-hour journey to get the right time from Greenwich until 1836 when John Belville started a service bringing Greenwich Time to makers' workshops. Many of Vulliamy's workbooks are to be found in the Public Record Office, deposited there because of a legal dispute.

He was one of few makers to make use of Harrison's

grasshopper escapement and examples can be found in the British Museum and in the Society of Antiquaries. However in his hands the escapement is quite differently designed and unmistakably his.

Watchman's Clocks

These clocks were sufficiently popular to warrant being exhibited in the 1851 Exhibition. E.J. Wood records this fact in his book *Curiosities of Clocks and Watches*, London 1866, p. 197. In his paragraph on the subject he refers to them as both 'detector' and 'tell-tale' clocks. He describes how they work and mentions one of the clocks in a lobby of the House of Commons.

Wood was a reporter not an horologist, but nevertheless his book is a mine of information packed with good things. However one does need to be cautious and critical when reading the book. As an example, he reports on a clock on p. 64 which, he says, goes for 100 years on a winding and said to belong to the Marquis of Bute at Luton Park, Bedford.

Grimthorpe in *Clocks, Watches and Bells*, has the following to say:

Tell-tale clock. This is said in one of the Parliamentary papers about the Westminster clock to be an invention of Mr. Whitehurst of Derby, for watching watchmen and telling whether they are on the watch and in the proper place all the night. That unpleasant little clock which one hears striking the quarters 3 or even 4 times in some Westminster Abbey sermons, is of this kind, and there are some in the lobbies of the Houses of Parliament. There are a set of spikes sliding in holes in a 24 hour dial, one for every quarter of an hour, which can be pushed in by pulling a handle in the clock case during a few minutes of that quarter only. So if any pin is found sticking out in the morning it indicates that the watchman was either asleep or away at the time belonging to that pin. The plate carries the inner ends of the pins over an inclined plate or roller at some other period of the 24 hours, which pushes them all out again ready for work the next night.

Thus we see that some of these clocks struck and also had a device for automatically resetting the pins.

In 1925 there was a sale in Southsea by Fleming & Co. Their advertisement was as follows:

Parliamentary relics from the Houses of Commons, Westminster. Interesting set of twelve Watchmen's tell-tale Grandfather Clocks. In oak cases with silver dials [silvered of course – author] twelve hours inscribed VR, six foot two inches high, fourteen inches wide and eight inches deep. Makers 6 by Messers. Dutton, London and 6 by Messrs Vulliamy dated 1846–1852. All in good going order. These clocks are the original set that did duty to the House of Commons and were placed in various parts of the building equidistant from one another. That enabled the watchman to record his visit every quarter of the hour on his rounds by having to pull a knob at the side that in turn pressed one of the pins in the edge of the dial out of sight . . . should a pin be left outstanding it silently recorded the watchman's lapse of duty.

It is interesting that the fact that these clocks were twelve hour is mentioned. Somehow Fleming knew that earlier clocks had been 24-hours and that these would possibly, therefore, not be as desirable as clocks with a more familiar type of time display.

79 *Spring-Driven Long-Case Clock*

by Parkinson & Frodsham, No. 640, *c.* 1900

An oak Gothic case carved with leaves and flanked with crocheted finials. The hood is arched and the arched waist door is carved with trefoils and flanked by flying buttresses. The base has quatrefoils.

The circular silvered dial is inscribed *Parkinson & Frodsham 15B Royal Exchange London 640* and has two levers, one for strike/silent and the other for eight bells/four bells. The hands are Gothic in design.

Most unusually all three trains of the movement are spring driven, there being gut fusees. It is quarter-striking on eight or four bells at choice. The clock is controlled by a pendulum and has an anchor escapement.

H. 7 ft 2 in (218 cm).

Some other long-case clocks have weight-driven going trains with the striking and chiming trains being spring driven.

William Parkinson & W.J. Frodsham
Both men were admitted into the Clockmakers' Company in 1802. Their business was then at 4 Change Alley, Cornhill, London.

They showed at the Great Exhibitions of 1851 and 1862, and were awarded a medal in the latter. They also exhibited in Paris in 1889.

In 1890 the business moved to 16 Queen Victoria Street and a year later moved to 35 Royal Exchange. After only another two years they moved yet again to 15B Royal Exchange, where they remained until 1905.

79

6 *Mantel and Table Clocks*

*D*espite the domination of the imported French mantel clock, many English examples were made. They were of high quality and of a quite surprising variety of styles. As can be seen in the following examples, almost every type of case top is represented: flat, arched, bell, architectural, to name but a few. Almost all have movements with fusees and are controlled by pendulums. None of the clocks in this section has a compensated pendulum, however, and mantel or bracket clocks with this refinement are to be found in the section 'Wall and Table Regulators' in Chapter 7.

The term 'bracket clock' is only used on one clock in this section. The term is really a misnomer; it should only be used for a clock with its own bracket. Clocks so termed are usually either mantel or table clocks.

It is not always easy to tell if a mantel clock is Victorian or not. The variation in the cases in this section is surprising. The Gothic type are, of course, peculiar to this era. Others are merely older styles copied. Yet more are a mixture of older styles and I suppose by this unmistakable as Victorian. Many, I fear, are over-embellished for modern taste and certainly offend the purists. There are also notable exceptions which are virtually impossible to classify as any particular style.

These mantel and table clocks are often what one might call semi-portable, some even being supplied with handles. There also may be fitted a locking device for the pendulum, so as to enable the clock to be moved without the pendulum having to be removed. This argues an ever-increasing involvement of owners with their clocks, for while there were professional clock winders to attend to the clocks in the household, no such device as a pendulum lock was really required. When the verge escapement was used in the clocks of the day a clock could be moved with ease and would quite often continue to go even as it was transported. However, by the time Victoria came to the throne the verge escapement was no longer in use; in fact many an older clock was converted from verge to the anchor escapement. These, now, are often converted back again.

The pendulum lock during this period often takes the form of a block fixed to the back plate in which is machined a groove into which the pendulum rod will just fit. The groove is slightly less in depth than the thickness of the rod so that this stands proud. It is then locked into position by a large headed screw normally kept in a threaded hole well away from the pendulum.

There are, however, some clocks in this section with lever platform escapements and these are, of course, as portable as a carriage clock. The development of the lever escapement had been going on apace in England since the turn of the century and by 1840 was almost in its final form, so that it is not surprising that it should be tried in clocks, and tried with great success. After all, the conditions of use are by no means as severe in a clock as in a watch, which has to perform when put into many different positions and when subjected to shock and vibration.

There may be many variations in case design evident in this section, but the situation with the movements is quite different. The chain fusee was mostly used; differences often lie in the striking. Chiming became very popular during this period and bells were still being used. The hour, however, was often struck on a coiled gong. Tubular bells were, of course, confined to the long-case clock and were not invented until the latter part of the century.

Those who, in the past, have tended to look down on the Victorian mantel clock as embodying much of what was worst about this period might be pleasantly surprised on looking through the following section.

80 *Timepiece with Alarm*

by Frodsham, Gracechurch Street,
London, 1854

Rosewood case inlaid with brass, gadrooned top
with carrying handle, bun feet.

Silvered dial of 3 in (7.6 cm) diameter
inscribed *FRODSHAM, Gracechurch Street
LONDON*. Gold moon hands with concentric
blued steel alarm setting band. The movement
with shaped plates, chain fusee and anchor
escapement.

H. 8¾ in (22 cm).

At no time while Frodshams were at
Gracechurch Street was the firm known simply
as Frodshams, but it is not difficult to guess that
the name on this clock means it was made in
1854, the only year when the name was not
associated with initials, a Christian name or the
name of another partner:

John Frodsham	1825–34	33 Gracechurch St.
John Frodsham & Son	1834–7	
John Frodsham & Son	1851–3	
Frodsham Son & Co.	1854	
Frodsham & Baker	1854–63	31 Gracechurch St.
Edward Frodsham	1864–81	
G.F. Frodsham & Co.	1882–8	
G.F. Frodsham & Co. Ltd	1888–1901	

Charles Frodsham & Co.

Charles Frodsham was born in 1810 and was
apprenticed to his father William James Frodsham. He
became a skilful watchmaker and worked at 7 Finsbury
Pavement. He joined with John Roger Arnold in 1843 at
84 Strand. The firm was known as Arnold & Frodsham
until about 1850 when Charles assumed sole control.
When Benjamin Lewis Vulliamy died in 1854 he
purchased this old-established firm and also became
Clockmaker to the Queen. He was Master of the
Clockmakers' Company in 1855 and in 1862. In 1861
he also purchased William Johnsonn's business.

He showed in the Paris Exhibition of 1855 when he
was given a Medaille d'Honneur. He also exhibited in
the International Exhibition in 1862 and was a juror at
the Paris Exhibition of 1867.

Upon Charles' death in 1871 the business at 84 the
Strand was sold to Harrison Mill Frodsham for £20,000

80

who continued to trade under the name of Charles
Frodsham & Co. In 1893 H.M. Frodsham sold the
business for £27,000 to a limited liability Company,
Charles Frodsham and Co. Ltd, and the firm's name still
survives today.

81 *Night Clock*

by J.W. Benson, London, *c.* 1890

A brass case with a bronze finish, a double-arch
top, a moulded base and bun feet. The dial is of
opalised glass with a fretted and engraved mask
and chapter ring. Incorporated into the mask
below the chapter ring is a monogram with the
letters *E.C.S.*, although, of course, not necessarily
in that order. Mounted in the second smaller arch
on the glass is a crown set with pastes.

The movement is a simple timepiece and lies behind the chapter ring thus leaving a space below for a lamp which when lit at night will shine through the glass dial so that the time can be read. The clock itself bears no signature but the fitted leather-covered travelling case does, namely *J.W. Benson*.

Night clocks have a long history. Pepys recorded one in the Queen's chamber (24 June 1664): 'After dinner to White Hall and there met with Mr. Pierce and he showed me the Queen's bedchamber where she had . . . with her clock at the bedside wherein a lamp burned that tells her the time of the night at any time.'

Early night clocks had an oil lamp that provided the illumination, with the result that the clock often caught fire. Consequently the survival rate is low. The invention of repeating work in about 1680, which allowed the owner to make the clock strike at will, did away with the necessity for these illuminated clocks although they still continued to be made, especially in Germany. English versions, such as this, are rare.

H. 7½ in (19 cm).

82 *Striking Mantel Clock*
by Frodsham, *c.* 1855

A mahogany case with canted corners and a shallow break-arch top. A rectangular door with an arch-top glazed aperture. The base has four ball feet. The front of the base, the door above the glazed aperture, the front of the arch top and the canted corners are all inlaid with brass. The sides of the case are fretted to let out the sound of the striking and above the frets are two carrying handles.

The arched dial is silvered with the inscriptions, numerals etc., painted on and much the worse for wear. The dial is inscribed *FRODSHAM LONDON*. Above the main dial is a subsidiary dial with *CHIME/SILENT*. Gold moon hands.

A twin chain-fusee movement with a recoil anchor escapement.

H. 14 in (35.6 cm).

81

82

83 A Group of Three Victorian Table Clocks

See colour plate VII.

All three are in mahogany cases but how different these are. The clock on the left is by Henry David of Liverpool. It has an architectural top, a round dial flanked by pilasters with carving top and bottom. There is also carving in the tympanum and below the dial. The case has bun feet.

The clock in the middle is by J. Price of Chatham. Here the case is finished with marquetry. The work just above the base is inlaid not only with woods but also with ivory. This clock displays the foolishness of dismissing all Victorian clocks as tasteless. The restrained elegance of this case would not shame any age!

The clock on the right is by French of the Royal Exchange. This is a carved Gothic case, the carving very glossy and dark. Perhaps not in the best of taste although one can admire the workmanship.

All three clocks strike, all have chain fusees. The clock in the middle looks as if some numerals are missing but this is simply due to difficulties with reflections when it was being photographed.

Measurements not available.

James Moore, John and William French

This well-known firm was at 86 Cornhill, Royal Exchange from 1839 to 1841, they then moved to 80 Cornhill and were there until 1845. In 1843 John French the son of James Moore French is also recorded as being at 80 Cornhill and from 1845 to 1847 also at 9 Royal Exchange. At this last address there was a William French from 1849 to 1875. In 1856 William was also at 25 Leadenhall Street.

Thus when one gets a clock like this which is merely signed *French Royal Exchange* one can have a date of anything between 1839 and 1875 and a decision about its date has to be made on stylistic grounds.

84 Three Mantel Clocks: a contrast in styles

See colour plate VIII.

On the left of the colour plate is a clock bearing the name *Pert Bally a Paris* on the enamel dial. However, it is in the style of a Cole strut clock. It is a striking clock with three subsidiary dials showing the day of the week, the date and the month. These are named in English. Was this a clock made to suit the English taste?

The clock in the middle (and below) has a very beautiful moulded glass case, again it is a striking clock. The gold hands are in the Gothic style and the enamel dial is inscribed *INGLETON*.

The clock on the right is, despite appearances, not a chronometer but a simple timepiece with a high quality platform escapement. It bears the name *DENT* on the enamel dial with the address *33, 34 Cockspur Street, LONDON* and the number *24069*. This is M.F. Dent and the clock was made in 1862. The case is of ebonised wood with a black enamelled carrying handle.

Measurements not available.

84 Glass case clock inscribed *INGLETON*.

85 *Ship's Bell Clock*

by Walker Younge, London, *c.* 1850

A mahogany case with band of rope carving framing the bezel and supported by simple foliate carved scroll above a gadrooned base.

The enamel dial of 6½ in (16.5 cm) diameter has centre seconds. Subsidiary sunk 24-hour dial with hand rotating anticlockwise. Blued steel hands of modified fleur-de-lis form with concentric gold date hand. At X o'clock a set striking lever. Inscribed *WALTER YONGE LONDON*.

Movement with twin chain-fusees striking full ship's bells including provision for the dog watch. The striking is on a single bell and controlled by a count wheel – hence the provision of a set striking lever to synchronise the striking with the time shown. Two hammers strike the bell with one being silenced as required by a pump action.

Lever platform mounted on the back plate.

H. 14 in (35.5 cm).

Courtesy of Sothebys

85

86 *Table Clock*

by John Bennett, Cheapside, London, 1851

This boldly carved case is of quite pleasing proportions. It was shown by Bennett at the Great Exhibition of 1851. The Art-Journal Illustrated Catalogue of the Exhibition stated that Bennett showed a large number of horological objects and particularly mentions 'a model watch on a large scale, constructed so as to show the most compact form of the modern timepiece, with all its many recent improvements'.

Measurements not available.

86

John Bennett F.R.A.S., later Sir John Bennett

John Bennett moved from Stockwell Street in 1846 in Clerkenwell and had a business at 64 and 65 Cheapside, London from 1846 to 1889. He was a common councillor 1860–8 and a sheriff in 1871; a year after this he was knighted; he died aged 81. He exhibited in the London Exhibition of 1862 when he received a medal,

Fig. 86a

CITY NOTABILITIES.

No. I.—THE SHERIFF WITH A MOST MONSTROUS WATCH.

First Part of King Henry IV., act 2, sc. 4.

Fig. 86b A caricature in *Punch* published after Bennett had been made a sheriff of London in 1871. I suppose it must be granted that it was quite witty to find such an apt quotation, this being from Henry IV Part One. It is a pity that the artist could not, at least, have shown the relative positions of the two hands correctly – to say nothing of their proportions!

and in the Paris Exhibition in 1878 when he was given a silver medal. He was also made a Chevalier of the Legion of Honour. We have a fine portrait of Sir John Bennett which shows a man easily mistaken for a poet (fig. 86a).

Charles Dickens had one of his clocks which was purchased by the Dickens Fellowship in 1966 and is now in the Dickens House in London.

On 14 September 1863 Dickens sent a letter to Bennett which went as follows:

Since my hall clock was sent to your establishment to be cleaned it has struck the hours with great reluctance and, after enduring internal agonies of a most distressing nature, it has now ceased striking altogether. Though a happy release for the clock, this is not convenient to the household. If you can send down a confidential person with whom the clock can confer, I think it may have something on its works that it would like to make a clean breast of.

This chiming clock is a large bracket clock with a heavily carved mahogany case and matching bracket. It has a white enamel dial about 10 in (25.5 cm) in

diameter and is signed *65 & 64 Cheapside London*. The triple chain-fusee movement has a dead-beat escapement and Whittington chimes, these sounding on eight bells, with a large separate hour bell.

Bennett was a great believer in advertising and fig. 86c shows a full page advert that he took out in the *Evening News* on 26 July 1881. The address is given at the top and beneath this is the record of his achievement at the Paris Exhibition (see above). The advertisement, in case it cannot be read, offers lever watches for £5, gold watches £10 for a lady's and £15 for a gentleman's. Presentation watches were 20–40 guineas, half chronometers in silver cases were 16–25 guineas, and gold chronometers were from 60 guineas. A quarter-chiming hall clock was 36 guineas but curiously a chiming clock in a handsomely carved case was only £28. A French striking clock, marble cased, was a mere 3 guineas.

II

BENNETT

65 AND 64, CHEAPSIDE

LONDON, E.C.

WATCHES.

PARIS EXHIBITION, 1878

SIR JOHN BENNETT

WAL

AWARDED A SILVER MEDAL

And Created a Chevalier of the Legion of Honour

FOR THE

EXCELLENCE OF HIS WATCHES.

Marine and Gold Chronometers, Chime Clocks and Astronomical Regulators.

CLOCKS.

TO CLOCK PURCHASERS

JOHN BENNETT.

Having just Completed Great Alterations in his *CLOCK SHOW ROOMS* Is enabled to offer to purchasers the Most Extensive Stock in London, Comprising—

CLOCKS

For the Drawing, Dining Rooms, and Presentation, Of the Highest Quality, and Newest Designs, at the Lowest Prices.

JOHN BENNETT,

WATCH AND CLOCK MANUFACTORY,

65 & 64 CHEAPSIDE

PRICE LISTS AND CATALOGUES POST FREE

£10.

IN RETURN FOR A £10 NOTE,

FREE AND SAFE BY POST, ONE OF

BENNETT'S LADY'S GOLD WATCHES,

PERFECT FOR TIME, BEAUTY, AND WORKMANSHIP.

WITH KEYLESS ACTION.

AIR TIGHT, DAMP TIGHT, AND DUST TIGHT.

65 & 64, CHEAPSIDE, LONDON.

GOLD CHAINS at MANUFACTURER'S PRICES.

P.O.O. to

JOHN BENNETT, 65 & 64, CHEAPSIDE.

£15.

IN RETURN FOR POST-OFFICE ORDER

FREE AND SAFE BY POST, ONE OF

BENNETT'S

GENTLEMEN'S GOLD KEYLESS WATCHES,

PERFECT FOR TIME, BEAUTY, AND WORKMANSHIP.

WITH KEYLESS ACTION,

AIR TIGHT, DAMP TIGHT, AND DUST TIGHT.

JOHN BENNETT, 65 & 64, CHEAPSIDE, LONDON.

BENNETT'S

DINING, DRAWING ROOM, AND HALL CLOCKS.

MARBLE CLOCKS	from £2	2	0
DITTO, STRIKING HOURS and HALF HOURS	3	3	0
DRAWING-ROOM CLOCKS of the NEWEST DESIGN	4	4	0
HALL CLOCKS in MAHOGANY, OAK or WALNUT CASES	12	12	0
CHIME CLOCKS in HANDSOMELY CARVED CASES	28	0	0

Estimates on Application.

MANUFACTORY, 65 and 64, CHEAPSIDE.

BENNETT'S

GOLD PRESENTATION WATCHES.

10 Guineas, 20 Guineas, 30 Guineas, 40 Guineas

BENNETT'S

GOLD CHRONOMETERS.

from 60 Guineas

£5.

IN RETURN FOR A £5 NOTE,

BENNETT'S LEVER WATCH,

SOUND, STRONG, AND ACCURATE, WITH

KEYLESS ACTION, AIR TIGHT, DUST TIGHT, AND DAMP TIGHT.

FIVE POUNDS NET.

Five per cent. discount to Teetotallers.

FREE AND SAFE BY POST.

BENNETT'S

KEYLESS HALF-CHRONOMETERS.

Compensated for variations of temperature, adjusted in positions with improved keyless-action.

Specially fitted for India.

In Gold .... 30 to 40 Guineas.

In Silver .... 16 to 25 Guineas.

Ditto for Ladies, with richly engraved Gold Cases and Dials, from .... 20 to 30 Guineas.

BENNETT'S

18-CARAT HALL-MARKED CHAINS

AND

CHOICE JEWELLERY.

Free and Safe for Post-Office Order.

BENNETT'S

KEYLESS WATCHES:

No key required,

AIR TIGHT, DAMP TIGHT, DUST TIGHT,

Silver .... 6 Guineas.... 8 Guineas.... 10 Guineas

Gold ..... 10 Guineas.... 12 Guineas.... 14 Guineas

Every Watch skilfully Examined, Timed, and its Performance Guaranteed.

SAFE AND FREE BY POST.

JOHN BENNETT'S

WATCHES:

	Guineas
GOLD CHRONOMETERS ....from	60
PRESENTATION GOLD WATCHES	20 to 40
LADIES' GOLD KEYLESS ACTION WATCHES	10
SILVER WATCHES, with keyless action	6
GOLD KEYLESS HALF-CHRONOMETERS	30 to 40
SILVER HALF-CHRONOMETERS ...	16 to 25
Half-Chronometers are compensated for variations of temperature, adjusted in positions, and Wind and Set Hands, without keys.	
ENGLISH HALL CLOCKS, chiming the quarters	36
RICHLY GILT DRAWING-ROOM CLOCKS, with classic designs.	
MARBLE DINING-ROOM CLOCKS, with Antique Bronzes.	
18-CARAT HALL-MARKED CHAINS and choice JEWELLERY.	

JOHN BENNETT'S

CLOCK AND WATCH MANUFACTORY,

65 and 64 CHEAPSIDE.

COUNTRY ORDERS attended to with the utmost care. Post-Office Orders, or Cheques, crossed London and Westminster Bank, to JOHN BENNETT, 65 and 64, Cheapside.

INDIAN ORDERS should be accompanied by remittances or London references.

SHIPPERS, CAPTAINS, and WHOLESALE BUYERS LIBERALLY TREATED.

INDIAN and ENGLISH RAILWAYS CONTRACTED WITH on the BEST TERMS.

BENNETT'S

HOUSE, OFFICE, AND SHOP DIALS,

EIGHT-DAY PIECES,

IN MAHOGANY, OAK OR ROSEWOOD CASES.

Warranted for perfect Time.

CASH PRICES.

12*in*......£3	3	0		16*in*......£7	10	0
14*in*...... 4	4	0		20*in*......10	10	0
15*in*...... 5	5	0		24*in*......15	15	0

Price Lists post free on application.

JOHN BENNETT'S

WATCH AND CLOCK MANUFACTORY

65 and 64, CHEAPSIDE, LONDON.

Fig. 86c

Opposite **Fig. 86d**

90 *Chiming Clock*

by Craighead & Webb, Royal Exchange, London, *c.* 1855

A mahogany case of Gothic style with heavily carved cresting with a fruit and flower motif. Above the moulded base the side panels terminate in scrolls. An opening door and a silvered dial with engraved spandrels, Roman numerals, and the signature *CRAIGHEAD & WEBB Royal Exchange LONDON*. Blued steel moon hands. Two subsidiary dials, that on the right chime/not chime, that on the left a rise and fall regulation dial.

The movement with three chain-fusees and an anchor escapement, a plain uncompensated pendulum. Signed on the back plate *CRAIGHEAD & WEBB Royal Exchange LONDON*. Chiming is on eight bells with the striking on a gong.

H. 10½ in (27 cm).

Craighead & Webb are recorded as being at the Royal Exchange from 1847 to 1861.

91 *Quarter-Chiming Bracket Clock*

by Cloud & Shapland, London, *c.* 1880

The rosewood case has a broken-arch top and is inlaid with brass. It has Corinthian pillars, topped by four flambeau finials and a pineapple finial on the top, all of ormolu. A reeded plinth sits on top of the moulded base and there are gadrooned feet.

The clock still has its original matching bracket.

The case sides are fitted with cast fretted ormolu panels to let out the sounds of the chiming and striking.

The arched dial has a matted centre and a silvered chapter ring; there are applied ormolu spandrels. There are three subsidiary dials, one for

90

91

regulation, one for strike/silent and the third for Westminster or Cambridge chimes. Between these subsidiary dials and the chapter ring is a shaped plate inscribed *Cloud and Shapland London.*

The triple fusee movement has an anchor escapement and a pendulum. It is fitted with rise and fall regulation. It chimes the quarters on eight bells and strikes the hours on a gong.

Measurements not available.

92 *A Gothic Quarter-Striking Table Clock*

by Hunt & Roskell, London, *c.* 1870

This fantastic piece has a gem-encrusted silver-gilt case in the shape of a pyx of Gothic form; a pyx is the box in which the consecrated host is kept or carried. The lower part of the case has blind arcading between cinquefoil friezing and the upper section is set with filigree scrollwork. The roof is naturalistically tiled. At each corner there are pinnacled columns of glass simulating rock crystal. The front is set with pearls and various hardstones around the gilt dial. The dial has enamel chapters and the hands are set with pastes.

The movement has twin chain-fusees, a lever escapement and quarter strikes on two gongs. It is signed *Hunt & Roskell* on the back plate.

H. 11¾ in (30 cm).

92

93 *Chiming Clock*

by Dent (M.F. Dent), London, *c.* 1880

The mahogany case has a bell top and stop fluted columns topped by ball finials. The sides are fretted; the base is moulded and there are bracket feet. Above the arch-top dial are two inset foliate spandrels.

The silvered chapter ring and three subsidiary dials are set in what is effectively a gilded pierced and engraved mask although this actually is built up from seven separate pieces which fit closely together. These are of very high quality.

The three subsidiary dials are from left to right chime/silent, slow/fast, chime on eight bells/ Westminster chime. Below the XII is *DENT TO THE QUEEN* and above the VI is *33 COCKSPUR ST LONDON*.

The three chain-fusee movement has an anchor escapement, a pendulum, rise and fall regulation and a pendulum lock.

H. 26 in (66 cm).

94

93

94 *Chiming Bracket Clock*

by William Connell, London, No. 787, *c.* 1850

The carved oak arched Gothic case has three finials. The silvered dial has engraved spandrels and two subsidiary dials in the Gothic arch. That on the left in the arch is the regulation dial *SLOW/FAST* and that on the right is *CHIME/SILENT*. Inscribed on the dial is *CONNELL, 83 Cheapside LONDON 787*.

The movement has three chain-fusees and chimes on eight bells. The hours are struck on a gong. There is an anchor escapement and pendulum locking is provided. The back plate is also signed as on the dial.

H. 31½ in (80 cm).

William Connell

Although it is not so signed, we know that this clock is by *William* Connell because he gives us his address.

William was free of the Clockmakers' Company in 1846. He was originally apprenticed to William Wright, a Brixton watchmaker. Connell was at 22 Middleton Street from 1839–1845 when he succeeded Richard Pinfold Ganthony at 83, Cheapside, (Ganthony was Master of the Clockmakers' Company for the second time in 1844).

Connell died in 1862 when he was succeeded by his son William George. They are recorded at the Cheapside address until 1875.

95 *Chiming Bracket Clock*

by John Moore & Sons, Clerkenwell, London, No. 11468, *c.* 1850

The ebonised case is inlaid with brass in the form of scrolling foliage and has fretted sides. There is heavily carved cresting. The shallow arched opening door at the front has bevelled plate glass.

The silvered dial has foliate and floral engraved spandrels. Within the chapter ring is inscribed *JOHN MOORE & SONS CLERKENWELL LONDON 11468*. Above the XII is *STRIKE/SILENT*. The hands are of blued steel.

The three chain-fusee movement has an anchor escapement, a pendulum, pendulum locking and chimes on eight bells, the hours being struck on a gong.

H. 17 in (43 cm).

For details of John Moore & Sons see Long-Case Clocks, p. 87.

95

96 *An Unusual Mahogany Calendar Table Timepiece*

Anonymous, *c.* 1880

The case is moulded broken arch, with a panel below with applied foliate decoration.

The circular painted dial is 10 in (25.5 cm) in diameter and has four subsidiary dials and a Halifax moon (i.e., a spherical moon in an aperture, one half of which is painted black and

96

Fig. (viii) Hall Regulator with carved mahogany Gothic case, listed in the Army and Navy Stores catalogue.

escapement with jewelled pallets and its mercurial pendulum. An example of a regulator taken from the catalogue issued by The Army and Navy Stores is shown in fig. viii. Colour Plate XII shows a chiming regulator, made by the famous firm of Smith & Sons of Clerkenwell.

Almost every famous horologist made regulators and they were produced in all the major clockmaking countries. Not all are made to stand on the floor or hang on the wall; there are also table regulators and although these are the exception to the rule some examples will be given later in the chapter.

Among the regulators that stand on the floor is a special type known as a journeyman's clock. These are a curious combination of 'portable/non-portable' clock and were made specifically for astronomers and surveyors who needed accurate time when working in the field. However, I have not come across one that was made in Victoria's reign so none can be included.

Since the regulator was a 'workhorse' there is a greater degree of uniformity in their appearance than in many other types of clocks. Illustrating clock after clock that looks almost exactly the same as the previous one seemed pointless so I have tended to pick the more unusual types of regulator. Some standard types will be present, however.

As a point of interest there is a Molyneux regulator clock illustrated in colour (plate XI) that Michael G. Cox is almost certain belonged to John Hartnup, who was very much involved with the Shepherd Chronometer described on pp. 51–53. Michael Cox wrote a most interesting article in the August 1981 edition of *The Connoisseur* describing the Molyneux regulator and another by William Cozens. The article was called 'Precision Timekeeping'.

The elimination of unnecessary friction is one of the important aims when constructing a regulator. To this end high numbers of teeth are used in the pinions since this leads to a smoother and more efficient transmission of power. There are often jewelled surfaces where the escape wheel acts on the pallets and also jewelled bearings at the faster moving end of the gear train. Something else that leads to losses in a conventional clock is the motion work which is extra gearing to be driven. This is why so many of the regulators have the type of dial layout that is actually given the description 'regulator'. The design is such that no motion work is required for there is a wheel in the train that revolves once in 12 hours (or sometimes 24), another that revolves once an hour and of course the usual once a minute – the seconds hand.

Thus the pivots of these gears have merely to be extended and have hands mounted upon them, this resulting in the regulator dial layout.

The greater efficiency of the regulator may be judged from the fact that the driving weight is often only a third of that in an ordinary long-case clock and can be as little as a quarter. This is only the case, however, when a conventional escapement is used, that is the dead-beat (or even sometimes the chronometer). There are examples that are fitted with the gravity type of escapement and these require an excess input of power that means a driving weight of the size to be found in a normal clock despite the care taken in construction. The gravity escapement eliminates any variations in power that arrive at the escape wheel but to do this successfully it must still work when the minimum force arrives. Thus it has to absorb anything over and above this which is equivalent to wasting it. Only in this way can it ensure a constant impulse to the pendulum.

102

103 *Long-Case Regulator*

by J. Shenfield, Manchester, *c.* 1840

A strikingly figured mahogany case with glazed rectangular door, panelled plinth and architectural hood with canted corners.

Silvered 'regulator' dial, jewelled dead-beat escapement and massive pendulum with wood rod/lead bob combination.

H. 6 ft 11½ in (212 cm).

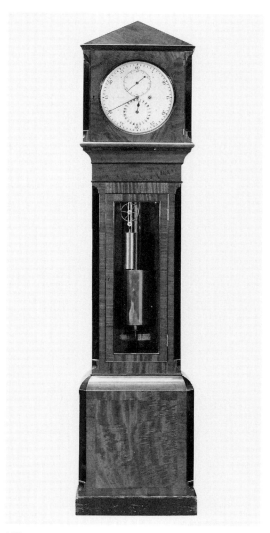

102 *A high quality Regulator Movement*

Anonymous

Every arbor pivot has a brass endpiece with the exception of those extended pivots that carry the hands.

The reflection in the front plate means the dead-beat escapement can be seen in its entirety. The movement has very thick plates and eight pillars. The massive back cock has vees to support the rod that passes through the top chops of the suspension spring.

The limiting screws on either side of the crutch prevent the escape wheel from being damaged by the pallets.

The arbor directly above the barrel is that of the maintaining ratchet. The maintaining power is of the Harrison type.

Measurements not available.

103

104 *Magnificent Long-Case Regulator*

by Cope & Molyneux of London, *c.* 1840

A rare example of Mudge's gravity escapement fitted to any clock. A plain well-figured mahogany case.

104

Fig. 104a

Fig. 104b

Fig. 104c

The dial is the normal regulator type with the exception that it is 24-hour. Fig. 104a shows the pendulum and its support fixed to the backboard. The rate can be adjusted from the top, overcoming the need to stop the clock while it is being regulated. This can be seen in fig. 104b which shows the clock and pendulum together from the side. The Y-shaped piece embraces the thickened part of the top of the pendulum rod but is friction tight. When the large knurled screw is turned it causes the rod to slide up or down with respect to the Y piece, hence lengthening or shortening the pendulum. Note the two-blade suspension spring spanning the regulation device.

The curious shaped piece just like a bow-tie in shape is where impulse is given. The vertical edges are rounded so as to lessen the friction with the impulse arms and to get over any lack of squareness between the components.

Fig. 104c shows a top view of the movement and the escapement. Note the six pillars and the substantial plates. The pallets are like divided dead-beat pallets, each pallet having its own arbor. The horizontal extensions are to give additional weight to the pallet for it is this weight that is lifted by the escape wheel and that in falling gives impulse to the pendulum. The black and white drawing shows the principle of the escapement. Although invented by Thomas Mudge no example by him is known. This is not, however, the first known; this is in a clock by Catherwood which is in the British Museum.

Measurements not available.

Cope & Molyneux
Cope & Molyneux were at 30 Southampton Row, Holborn, when this clock was built.

George & Francis Cope & Co.
This firm was at 79 Alfreton Rd., Radford, Nottingham from 1845 to 1877. In 1881 they supplied a clock to Nottingham Exchange and in about 1850 a clock was made for Sneinton Parish Church which is now in the Industrial Museum, Wallaton Hall, Nottingham.

105 *Long-Case Regulator*
by Straub, London, *c.* 1845

The clock has a well-figured mahogany case. The trunk has an arched door and the plinth is panelled. The shallow break-arched hood seems small for the clock. The typical regulator dial is round and is silvered.

Measurements not available.

Michael Straub is recorded as a clockmaker at 53½ Chiswell St., in 1845 and at 13 Barbican in 1847.

105

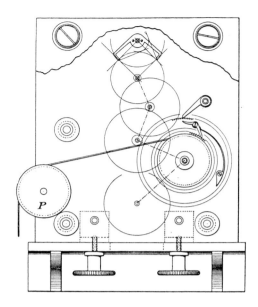

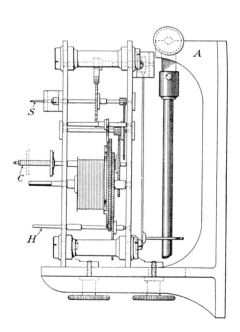

106 *Eight-Day Long-Case Regulator*

by Molyneux & Sons, London, *c.* 1850

See colour plate XI

The case has a carcase of mahogany veneered in lightly marked woods. There is a glazed door and a panelled plinth. The top has a shallow architectural hood. The weight drops to the side of the pendulum. There is a beat plate mounted on the backboard.

The dial is circular and of regulator design. It is inscribed *Molyneux & Sons London*; there is a 24-hour dial.

The six-pillar movement has a high count gear train, a dead-beat escapement with jewelled pallets and Harrison's maintaining power. There is a jewelled endstone to the pallet arbor and a jewelled bearing in the front plate for the escape wheel arbor. The movement is furnished with dust covers.

There is a mercurial pendulum with a glazed jar and a beat setting facility.

H. 6 ft 6 in (198 cm).

Robert Molyneux
Robert Molyneux was joined by his sons in 1830, having established his own business in about 1800. He was an important figure, being named an adjudicator to the Board of Longitude in 1805. With the introduction of the Premium Trials in 1832 he entered chronometers regularly. His firm mostly made chronometers and regulators.

Examples of his work can be found at the Royal Observatory at the Cape of Good Hope and Brussels; two regulators at Bidston Observatory, Liverpool, and one at the United States Naval Observatory, Washington.

Fig. 105a A typical regulator movement with a massive cast iron bracket 'A' which supports the movement and the pendulum. The escapement is dead beat and the weight line is taken off to the side via pulley 'P'; Harrison's maintaining power is fitted. 'S' is the seconds pivot, 'H' the hour and 'C' is the cannon pinion that carries the minute hand.

107 *Striking Long-Case Regulator with Calendar and the Age and Phase of the Moon*

by Thomas Morgan of Manchester, *c.* 1860

This is a remarkably complex clock for a regulator and must really be considered as a borderline example. The case is of walnut and above the panelled plinth is glazed at the front and sides and around the arched top. There is carved fretwork below the circular dial.

The dial has no less than six subsidiary dials and is laid out in a regulator fashion. The main dial is a centre seconds dial with the hour dial at 9 o'clock, and the minute dial at 3. At 6 o'clock is the date dial with the signature on either side of it. At 12 o'clock is the month dial with, on its right, the day of the week dial and on the left the dial showing the age and phase of the moon.

The substantial movement has a dead-beat escapement and maintaining power. The pendulum has wood rod/lead bob type compensation.

The weights are brass covered as is the pendulum bob.

H. 6 ft 6 in (1.98 m).

108 *Eight-Day Regulator*

by James Brock and with Denison's Five-legged Escapement, 1864

The moulded arch-topped case is of mahogany and has a glazed door running from top to bottom of the case. The silvered dial, 12 in (30.5 cm) in diameter, is of an unusual layout, this being dictated by the layout of the movement which is effectively made upside down. As can be seen in fig. 108a the dial is uncommon because it has the hours and the seconds subsidiary dials in the lower half of the main minute dial. Note that, unusually, the seconds hand rotates in two minutes and that the divisions are of two seconds. As the escapement is single beat the hand will move forward in two-seconds jumps so that this dial is eminently sensible.

In the upper half is a circle engraved with the maker's name and the fact that the clock has Denison's Gravity Escapement. The case has the usual beat plate and in addition a plaque stating that the clock was designed by Lord Grimthorpe (then Edmund Becket Denison) and is described in his book *Clocks, Watches and Bells* (p. 106, seventh edn.).

The movement and pendulum are mounted on a massive steel bracket. The pendulum is unusual in that the bob is screwed up or down to effect adjustments (fig. 108b). The rod is held by the capstan arm and the bob turned with the amount it is moved being indicated on its divided top. The pendulum has roller suspension.

The movement has spotted plates bearing evidence of much alteration and, therefore, must be considered an experimental clock. Fig. 108c shows the back of the movement with the crutch and the adjustable pins that embrace the pendulum rod. These can be arranged so impulse can be disposed about the dead point as desired, only possible because the escapement is single beat.

Fig. 108d shows the movement looking up from underneath. The escape wheel with its five teeth, or legs, is clearly seen as is the nib of the detent on the left. The detent is unlocked by a click which trips over the detent when the pendulum goes to the right in the drawing. When the pendulum returns to the left the click pushes

108

Above **Fig. 108a**; right **Fig. 108c**

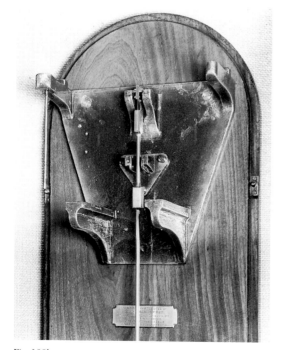

Fig. 108b

Fig. 108d

the detent aside, the escape wheel turns and a pin gives impulse. The position of the pallet on the crutch which receives impulse from the pin is critical.

Returning to fig. 108c, a surprise is the fact that there are lantern pinions in the train of gears. These are on the second and minute hand arbors.

My comment on this escapement is that there is in fact little point in it and it is predated by much more practical examples of chronometer-type constant force escapements such as is to be found in the later example by Edward Funnel of Brighton in Chapter 8, Skeleton Clocks.

H. 5 ft 7 in (170 cm).

James Brock

James Brock had three addresses in George Street, Portman Square, from 1857 to 1881, Nos. 18, 21 and 64.

He showed in the 1862 Exhibition when he received an Honourable Mention and died in 1893 aged 67.

Details of Denison's life are to be found in the Chapter on Turret Clocks, pp. 164–183.

109 *Chiming Regulator*

by Smith & Sons, *c.* 1880
See colour plate XII

An imposing mahogany case, the hood with a pagoda top. There are finials on either side of the bottom of the hood. The trunk is flanked by large and heavily carved pilasters. There is a glazed door with an arch top. The plinth is panelled with smaller panels on either side which are outset and act as a continuation of the pilasters.

The silvered dial is round and bears the inscription *SMITH AND SONS, ST JOHNS SQUARE, CLERKENWELL.* There are three subsidiary dials, one for the seconds, one for *strike/silent* and another *full-chime/Westminster.* Through the glazed door one can see the mercurial pendulum and the three brass-cased weights. There is a beat plate on the back of the case.

H. *c.* 7 ft (213 cm).

For details of this firm, see the English Carriage Clock Chapter, pp. 16-39.

110 *Skeletonised Long-Case Regulator*

by Elkington, *c.* 1880

Most people do not associate skeletonisation with long-case clocks but here is a superb example of a skeletonised regulator with a double three-legged gravity escapement of the same type as is used in Big Ben (see fig. 110a). The clock has a mercurial pendulum. The case is of superb quality with an arched top and glazed down to the plinth. The plinth is very deep and has a finely figured decorative panel.

The driving weight is taken off to the side so that it clears the pendulum. This is to prevent sympathetic motion being imparted to the weight by the pendulum bob swinging near to it. If this happens there is an effect on the swings of the pendulum, with a resultant upset to the timekeeping. Ideally the weight should drop in a separate chamber. It will be noted that the weight is large in this clock supporting the remarks made in the introduction to this chapter.

Although this clock bears the name of Elkington it was probably made for them by Dent and may well have been Elkingtons' shop regulator.

Measurements not available.

Elkington & Co. Ltd

The chronology of this firm is as follows:
B.R. Elkington & Co., from 1836 (or before) to 1842
Elkington Mason & Co., (otherwise Elkington & Co.,) 1842–61
Elkington & Co., 1861–86
Elkington & Co. Ltd 1887–1963
The success of this well-known company of electroplaters and silversmiths was due initially to the energy and drive of George Richard Elkington who was born in 1801. The story of his many businesses and partnerships is too complicated to recount here, the single most important thing about the firm is that they were the original patentees of the electroplating process and eventually brought it to perfection. The deciding factor was the invention of an electrolite containing potassium cyanide.

In 1843 a patent was taken out for the electroplating of flowers and other organic objects. In the early 1860s,

110

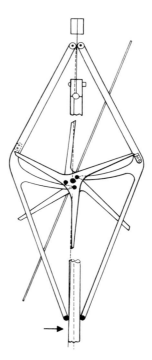

Fig. 110a

it may surprise readers to learn, a patent was taken out for the production of items made from Parkesine, a compound of pyroxiline now commonly known as Zylonite or celluloid.

Elkington's vast output in the century following 1840 included all types of silver and electroplate, from tableware to fine display and art works. They also made bronzes and bronze imitations. In the late 1890s they perfected techniques of electroplating on glass and porcelain.

As retailers Elkington were supplied by a number of manufacturing silversmiths and these makers' marks are often found overstruck with Elkington's mark.

Elkington were one of the most frequent exhibitors at national and international exhibitions including nearly all of those mentioned in the section on exhibitions. They were also in the Franco-British Exhibition in London in 1908 and the Brussels Exhibition in 1910. They were most unlucky at this last exhibition since there was a fire which devastated their display which was reduced to half a ton of scrap-metal, a mixture of gold, silver and nickel. This must have been a severe blow to the firm since obviously many of their finest pieces would have been on show.

III *Mahogany Long-Case Regulator*

by Gillett & Johnston, Croydon, *c.* 1900

This clock is most unusual in that it has digital display for the hours and minutes. The day, month and date show in apertures below the hours and minutes. At the top of the dial is the subsidiary seconds dial.

The dial has the inscription *Gillett & Johnston, Croydon*.

The arch-top case has a plain panelled plinth and a glazed door that also shows the pendulum and weights (not in the case in the photograph). The weights are carried to the side on rollers and the pendulum has zinc and steel compensation. Note the holes drilled in the outer tube to allow free circulation of the air. This is to allow the pendulum to react to temperature changes as quickly as possible.

The massive movement has a dead-beat escapement.

H. 6 ft (183 cm), W. 18 in (46 cm).

Gillett & Johnson
In the 1885 Exhibition the firm, incorrectly called Gillett & Co., were recorded as having exhibited, among other things, this type of clock which they called the 'chronoscope'. The firm felt that the digital display was especially applicable to railway timekeepers and for giving 24-hour time. They would be pleased to see that this is now the norm on all our main line stations.

Zinc and Steel compensation pendulum

In the zinc and steel compensation pendulum the rod and the outside tube are of iron or steel and the bob rests upon the collar of the outer tube. Linking the two is a tube of zinc. It is preferable for the bob to be centre-supported since the greater mass of the bob means that it responds to a change of temperature more slowly than the rod assembly, so its contribution to the compensation is best kept neutral. Big Ben has a pendulum of this type.

In 1886 Thomas Buckney of Dents read a paper to the Royal Astronomical Society entitled 'On the Superiority of Zinc and Steel Pendulums' when he detailed experiments he had done to demonstrate that mercurial pendulums were

111

much more sluggish in their response to a change in temperature than were zinc and steel pendulums. He also described how the degree of compensation could be adjusted by the astronomer on site without difficulty. The method used was the subject of patent No. 9358 taken out by Buckney in 1885. The idea was to have a nut threaded externally and internally which connected the two tubes and could thus be a fine adjustment for their relative positions. Varying their relative positions would, of course, affect the degree of compensation.

Wall and Table Regulators

A wall regulator is in general little different to a long-case regulator as far as its mechanism is concerned. It still has a seconds pendulum and the movement can be identical in size to that in a long-case presentation.

Table regulators are, however, a breed of their own and are very special and relatively rare. How well they would perform would to a large extent depend upon where they were put for they need a stable surface on which to sit. They were doubtless more a prestige item than anything since if one really needed an accurate portable timekeeper the sensible choice would be a chronometer.

112

112 *Eight-Day Table Regulator*

by E.J. Dent, London, No. 860, *c.* 1840

The gilded-brass base supports four pillars with a pediment surmounted by the clock mechanism. The pendulum is supported by an A frame which lies behind the clock mechanism.

The 4 in (10 cm) diameter silvered dial has a subsidiary seconds dial and is inscribed *DENT London 860*. It is similarly signed on the back plate.

The blued steel hands are of spade design with the hour tip being skeletonised. The seconds hand is also of blued steel.

The movement has a chain fusee with maintaining power and has gilded plates and wheels. The train is jewelled throughout. The escapement is a delicate Graham dead-beat with

Fig. 112a

jewelled pallets and is furnished with beat adjustment. Fig. 112a shows the beautifully spotted plates and the beat adjustment and regulator-style chops are plainly visible. Note the collar part way down the pendulum rod; this is used for fine adjustment of the rate. The half-second pendulum requires the 60 tooth escape wheel one can see if a normal seconds dial is to be used. The most unusual half-second mercurial pendulum has a steel jar and is fitted with a large diameter rating nut. There is a degree scale on the base top.

H. 18½ in (47 cm).

Clock No. 522 by Dent looks superficially similar but is not the same mechanically for it has a remontoire and the train is not jewelled throughout.

113 *Eight-Day Wall-Mounted Regulator*

by Thomas Cooke & Sons, London and York, *c.* 1880

The rectangular glazed case is of oak. The 24-hour regulator-type dial is typical of the work of Cooke with its black painted finish. The movement and the pendulum are supported by a bracket screwed to the backboard. There is a false backboard and the weight is behind this, the line being led behind by a pulley system. The grid-iron pendulum has a massive lenticular bob. There is a beat plate which, it should be noted, is upside down in the photograph.

The movement has tapering plates and the pillars are secured by screws. The four-wheel train is of high count and the dead-beat escapement has jewelled pallets. The maintaining power is of the sun and planet variety as favoured by Cooke.

H. 4 ft 7 in (140 cm).

Thomas Cooke & Sons
T. Cooke & Sons were at the Buckingham Works in York and showed in the International Exhibition of 1862 when they obtained a medal. It was reported that Cooke 'distinguished himself for judicious form and adoption, both in the great work and escapement for turret machinery'.

114 *Wall Regulator*

by Charles Frodsham, London, No. 983,
c. 1865

Elegance indeed! The rosewood case has ormolu mounts. The hood has an arched top with glazed sides and is topped by an ormolu bow. The glazed door at the front is rimmed with a brass moulding. Beneath the hood is a frieze of ormolu with leafy scrolls and cartouches. Beneath this again is a shallow apron of acanthus leaves, again in ormolu.

The trunk is glazed all round and the door frame has brass edging inside and out.

The dial is set out in regulator fashion and is gilded and engraved all over. Beneath the minute ring is a cartouche with the inscription *CHAS FRODSHAM 84 STRAND LONDON No 983*. There are also three rondels in the same area which carry the following inscriptions: both left and right is repeated; *BY APPOINTMENT TO THE QUEEN CHAS FRODSHAM LONDON*. In the centre is *GOLD MEDAL OF HONOUR PARIS EXHIB 1855*.

The weight-driven movement (fig. 114a) has Harrison's maintaining power. Both the movement and the pendulum are supported by a cast-iron bracket. The wheels have six crossings. There is a jewelled endplate to the rear end of the escape pivot and jewel holes to the pallet pivots. The dead-beat escapement has jewelled pallets.

The seconds mercurial pendulum has a glazed jar and there is beat regulation at the top of the crutch.

Measurements not available.

For details of Charles Frodsham see Mantel and Table Clocks, p. 95.

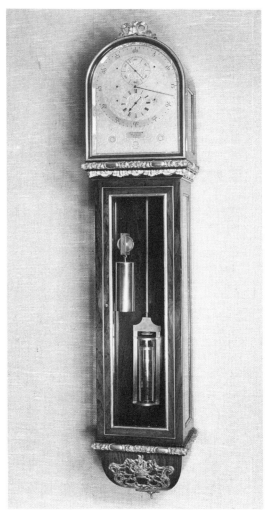

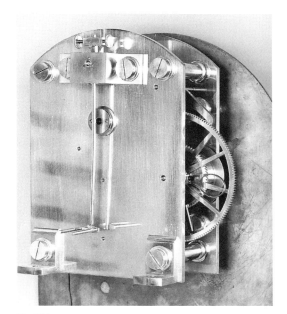

Fig. 114a

114

115 *Wall Regulator with a Double Three-Legged Gravity Escapement*

Anonymous, *c.* 1880

The mahogany case shows the Gothic influence in the shape of the arch in the top of the glazed aperture in the door. There is an arch top to the case which has a concave moulded base with a turned finial. There are windows on either side of the case and the door runs from top to bottom.

The dial is typical for a regulator but the seconds hand being below the dial centre gives away the fact that this clock has a gravity escapement. The weight is even larger than one would expect since the restriction in height has required the use of a double pulley above the weight. One can tell this since the cord is led around the weight pulley and then back down again to the pulley frame. Although one needs, all else being equal, only two-thirds of the drop for the same length of run the weight has to be half as heavy again.

Note what looks like a washer just over halfway up the pendulum rod. This is a weight tray and provides a way of fine regulating the clock without the need to stop it. If small weights are put on this tray the result will be a slight gain since the effective centre of gravity has been raised. Thus when the clock is being regulated using the rating nut one stops when the rate is slightly slow so that the final regulation can all be done using the weights which are often those used in chemical weighing balances.

Measurements not available.

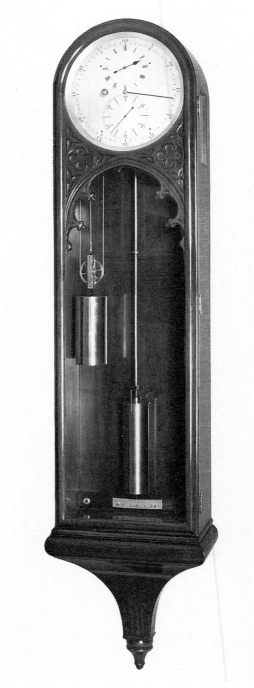

Plate I, cat. no. 1

Plate II, cat. no. 16

Plate III, see cat. no. 35

Opposite **Plate IV**, cat. no. 42 (the clock on the pile of books)

Plate V, cat. no. 50

Opposite **Plate VI**, cat. no. 51

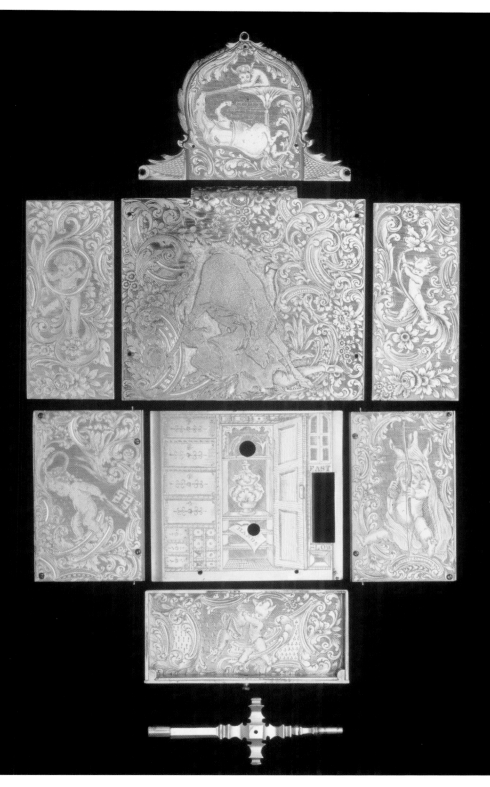

Plate VII, cat. no. 83

Plate VIII, cat. no. 84

Opposite **Plate IX**, cat. no. 99

Plate X, cat. no. 100

Opposite left **Plate XI**, cat. no. 106; opposite right **Plate XII**, cat. no. 109

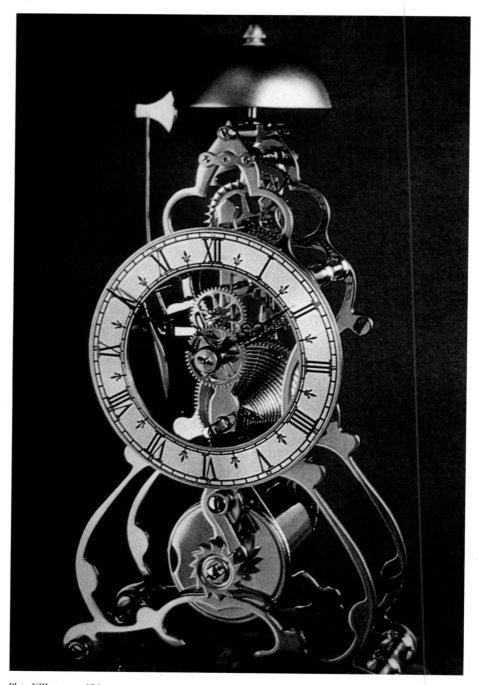

Plate XIII, cat. no. 124

Opposite **Plate XIV**, cat. no. 126

Plate XV, cat. no. 134

116 *Miniature Wall Regulator*
by A. Crawford Largs, London, *c.* 1870

The mahogany case has a shallow plinth below a chamfered trunk door with an inset panel and a hood with chamfered angles and an architectural top.

The silvered and engraved rectangular dial is only 9¼ × 5¼ in (23.5 × 13.3 cm) and is signed *A CRAWFORD LARGS*, there is a large seconds dial in the top half with a conventional hour and minute dial below.

The weight-driven movement has Harrison's maintaining power, a dead-beat escapement of the Vulliamy pattern (see fig. 116a) and a wood rod/lead bob pendulum. The pendulum is supported by a cast-iron bracket fixed to the backboard. A beat scale is provided.

H. 4 ft 9 in (145 cm).

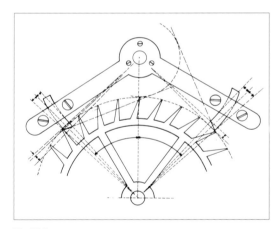

Fig. 116a

117 *Wall Regulator with Calendar and Phases and Age of the Moon*

by Arthur Kinder, 1899

This clock, I think, must be admired for its sheer elegance, although I realise these things are a question of personal taste. The case is of figured mahogany with restrained stringing. It is glazed at front and sides and has a broken-arch top and dial.

The dial is gilded with silvered chapter rings and a silvered rondel in the arch. There are fine quality spandrels. Around the outside of the rondel is *Arthur Kinder fecit A.D. 1899* with a crest and motto at its centre on a blue ground.

The main part of the dial is arranged in regulator fashion with a central minute hand, a minute ring numbered every five minutes and four subsidiary dials. At 6 o'clock is the hour dial, at 12 o'clock the large seconds dial with in its upper part an aperture showing the phases of the moon (caught in the photograph at an unfortunate time since it is new), in a small cut-out at the top of this aperture the age of the moon is shown – it is 1. The dial at 3 o'clock is for the date, that at 9 o'clock is the day of the week and the month is shown in a small aperture at the bottom of the rondel in the arch.

The massive movement is supported by a heavy bracket which can be seen through the top part of the door aperture. The escapement is dead beat. The driving weight is taken off to one side so that as it falls it does not interfere with the swing of the pendulum. The effective drop of the weight has been increased by taking the cord back up and down again to the centre of the elegant pulley and this gives the equivalent of one-and-a-half times the fall one would get with the ordinary arrangement. The pendulum is mercurial in glass, supported by a frame and with the regulation nut above the bob. A silvered beat plate shows just over 2½ degrees either side of zero.

Measurements not available.

117

The Mercurial Pendulum

While experimenting with mercury in December 1721 Graham was impressed with the relatively large amount of expansion that occurred with a rise in temperature. Thereafter he began his trials using a glass jar containing the mercury as the bob of a pendulum. He obtained, by experiment, the height of mercury in the jar such that its upward movement exactly compensated for the downward movement of the steel pendulum rod and its suspension spring. He compared the rates of two good quality clocks, one with an uncompensated pendulum and the other with his new mercurial pendulum; this was done over a period of more than three years.

Graham found that the errors of the uncompensated pendulum were six times that of his mercurial version. Although this is no more than we would expect I still feel that Graham would have been surprised if he had known just how long his pendulum would continue to be used. In fact the arrangement as originally designed by Graham has its drawbacks, this is because the mass of mercury takes longer to respond to a change in temperature than the slender rod does. To help to overcome this the end of the rod can be dipped into the mercury. Putting the mercury into a glass jar does nothing to help in this direction either since glass is a poor conductor of heat; where performance is more important than appearance the mercury is put into a steel container.

More can be done by modifying the way in which the mercury is distributed. One arrangement is to split the mercury into two or even more jars.

Riefler made a pendulum in which the whole rod is the mercury container. The rod is a steel tube of about 1 mm wall thickness and a bore of 16 mm. It is filled with mercury for about two-thirds of its length. The bob is lenticular.

118 *Month-Going Wall Regulator*

by Brock of 64 George Street, Portman Square, London, *c.* 1880

This regulator is by James Brock who, before he set up on his own, was Dent's foreman and as such without doubt a superlative workman. He is known to have been at the address as on this clock from 1875. The rather severe design of case has a type of architectural top with a similar shape at the bottom. The white enamelled dial is round and of the usual regulator layout, it has the signature at the bottom *BROCK 64 GEORGE S. PORTMAN SQE LONDON.* The large driving weight indicates the fact that the clock runs for longer than usual.

The chief interest of this clock lies in its pendulum which has an unusual type of compensation for a regulator of this date. The combination is wood rod and lead bob. The ideal choice for the wood of which a pendulum rod should be made is a piece of straight-grained deal. Wood, to be satisfactory, must be made impervious to moisture and to this end may be either gilded or varnished. The bob must be about 12 in (30.5 cm) in length to effectively compensate for the normal coefficient of expansion of the wood, but this must be a matter of trial and error if the best results are to be achieved. The large diameter of the rod may occasion some surprise but the diameter must be at least ½ in (13 mm) if satisfactory fixings are to be made at either end of it. Sound end fixings are almost impossible to achieve with deal rods in smaller clocks and for this reason they are usually made of teak, ebony or mahogany. Ebony was a favourite with Vulliamy, although it is noticeable that in general he did not bother to make use of the compensating combination for his bobs were centre-mounted. See also my comments on p. 87. He was content to make use of the fact that the coefficient of expansion of wood is low, about a third of the other metals normally used in horology if one ignores Invar, not invented until the turn of the century.

Measurements not available.

The illustration of this clock is to be found in a group photograph in the Chapter on English Dial Clocks, p. 76.

8 Skeleton Clocks

*I*n the late eighteenth and early nineteenth century a new type of clock was developed, the skeleton clock. The English made this type of clock peculiarly their own, manufacturing them chiefly between 1820 and 1914, with production at a peak probably from 1860 to 1880.

This type of clock appealed to the Victorians because of their great interest in all things mechanical and here we have a clock that is not only under a glass dome, making its movement completely visible, but additionally has skeletonised plates thus revealing its most intimate secrets! Furthermore we are dealing with an era when items under glass domes were very common: wax fruit, stuffed birds, imitation flowers, etc., so that a clock under a glass dome fitted in very well.

Because of the high visibility of the mechanism the movements had to be finished to a high standard and as a result these clocks were never cheap. In the 1865 catalogue of S. Smith & Sons of Clerkenwell, a simple timepiece cost £2 10s. and a clock made in the likeness of York Minster was £10 – £12. The other clockmaking nations made these clocks but only in small quantities, except that is, strangely enough, for the Swiss who made hardly any.

At least half of all the skeleton clocks produced were made in Clerkenwell although this fact is not evident if one merely goes by the names to be found on the clocks. The reason for this is that they are merely the name of a retailer. Many would not buy a clock if it had just a trade-mark on it let alone a maker's name. Of course a skeleton clock movement with its high visibility could not be marked as discreetly as other types of clock, although I cannot myself see why they could not have been named, say, under the plate bottom edge. Clocks were often sold as ready-made kits, well-known suppliers being Smith & Sons of Clerkenwell and Haycocks of Ashbourne, Derbyshire. They offered a wide range of dials (also often skeletonised) and frame patterns. Many of these designs are recorded and when used as a reference can help to trace the origin of a clock.

Domes In 1856 W. E. Chance of Oldbury offered over 200 different types of dome. Only a fraction of this quantity is available today so that the breakage of a dome is a serious matter. It might be thought that one solution is to buy a dome already holding a display of dried flowers, since these are likely to be worth a lot less than a completed skeleton clock. However, check very carefully that all the dimensions are correct for although the height and width may be correct the dome may well be too shallow from front to back. Even if one finds a dome it is unlikely to fit the base that will no doubt already be with the clock so that at the very least the clock will have to be fitted to the new base. If there is no base with a second-hand dome then a base will have to be made and this will be an expensive business especially if it is to be done in a sympathetic manner. Some bases of wood may be capable of modification but to alter a marble base will again be an expensive exercise. To have to discard a marble base would of course be a great shame.

Plates Most production models had their brass plates cast. The casting of brass had been perfected by Victorian times and it is unusual to find a blow hole in these plates, which were hand finished and then polished and either lacquered or gilded. Almost certainly only one-off versions would have had their plates fretted from the solid.

There were two main types of design of plate, those dominated by scrollwork and the architectural. Some of the first type could be identified as representing a particular plant and some of the second type were recognisable as being specific buildings, namely cathedrals such as St Paul's, York Minster or Westminster Abbey or buildings such as the Brighton Pavilion or Scott's Memorial. This last was a design exclusive to one maker, W. F. Evans of the Soho Factory, Birmingham. One was shown by him at the Great Exhibition of 1851 and is now with the City Museum Art Gallery, Birmingham. Eighteen English makers showed 22 skeleton clocks in this exhibition, but only three makers from other countries.

One of the most impressive clocks to be shown was that by John Moore & Sons of Clerkenwell, see p. 87, and see fig. (ix). It is referred to by F. B. Royer-Collard in his definitive book, *Skeleton Clocks*, London 1969, when neither the details of its mechanism or its whereabouts were known. It is in fact in the entrance to the boardroom of the Norwich Union in Norwich and has been there since 1878. It has been described in detail in one of the house magazines of the Norwich Union Insurance Group which tells us that:

Fig. (ix) The caption in the *Art-Journal Illustrated* catalogue reads, 'Messrs. B. R. & J. MOORE, of Clerkenwell, exhibit an eight-day CLOCK, with lever escapement, striking the quarters and hours on fine cathedral-tone bells. The plate upon which the clock stands is steel, highly polished and enamelled.'

This clock was made for the Great Exhibition of 1851, and is one of the finest specimens of workmanship in existence. It chimes the quarters upon eight bells and strikes the hours on a ten-inch hemispherical bell concealed in the base; it also discharges each hour a very finely contracted machine playing twelve operatic selections; all the pinions are finished in the same manner as the best astronomical regulators, and the greatest accuracy is displayed in the fashion of every other portion. The frames are very massive, and having been polished and lacquered, were afterwards enamelled by a process then only known to the makers of the clock. The escapement is a finely constructed dead beat, and the pendulum has a steel rod and polished steel plates under enamelled and gilt rosettes. The clock is supported upon four pedestals standing upon a polished steel plate, which rests upon a massive carved walnut stand. It was one of the clocks which gained for Messrs John Moore & Sons, a Medal for excellence, and by the most competent Judges was considered the best specimen in the Exhibition.

It is thought that two other clocks like this were made and that one is in Russia and the other is in the USA.

Skeleton clocks shown at the Great Exhibition of 1851

(Details as given in the catalogue published at the time.)

EDWARDS, JAMES, STOURBRIDGE
An 8-day timepiece with an engraved glass dial plate, a crystal-cut pendulum ball and cut-glass centres to the wheels. A second clock the same but going for three months.

EVANS, WILLIAM F.
A 'Walter Scott monument clock'.

FELTHAM, R.D. OF KING STREET, ST HELIER, JERSEY
A 500-day clock with a compound pendulum.

GOWLAND, JAMES
A clock with an improved compensation pendulum.

HARVEY OF STIRLING, SCOTLAND
A clock with one wheel striking work.

LAMB, J., BICESTER, OXFORDSHIRE
A 400-day clock.

MAPPLE, D.D., 17 HULLS PLACE, JOHN'S ROW, ST LUKE'S.
A timepiece with improved lever escapement and improved clock winder.

MOORE & SONS
A chiming clock to go a month; and a second clock.

PACE, J.
A 3-year clock with six barrels. A pyramidal 3-month clock with a Graham dead-beat escapement.

PIKE, H. C., 9 CUMBERLAND ROW, ISLINGTON GREEN
A 400-day clock with a chronometer escapement to show dead seconds.

RIX, ISAAC, CONDUIT STREET, WESTBOURNE TERRACE
A skeleton chronometer beating 3 seconds, the pendulum being free for 2 out of the 3 seconds [exactly what this means is not clear!].

ROBINSON, P., BISHOP AUCKLAND
A temperature-compensated clock in the form of the clock tower and entrance to the Bishop of Durham's Palace at Bishop Auckland.

SHEPHERD, CHARLES, 53 LEADENHALL STREET
A skeleton magnetic striking clock showing how the number of blows to be struck is regulated.

SMITH & SONS, JOHN LANCELOT, WILLIAM STREET, JOHN'S SQUARE.
A year calendar clock and another chiming clock, chiming on 8 bells and striking on a gong.

TAFFINDER, ROTHERHAM
An 8-day clock in the form of Rotherham Cathedral and with a lever escapement.

THORNELOE, C., LITCHFIELD.
A month clock, quarter striking in the form of Litchfield Cathedral. Also a Gothic clock.

TRITCHLER, J., 402 OXFORD STREET, WESTBOURNE TERRACE
An 8-day clock with improved pendulum.

YOUNG, KNARESBOROUGH
A timepiece.

Technical details   As can be seen from the above list there is a great variety in the technical aspects of these skeleton clocks. Although admittedly we are looking at items for display in an exhibition the variety is really quite surprising. Among the durations we have everything from 8 days to three years! The escapements represented are: recoil, dead beat, detached lever, the chronometer, and to cap it all, a Patent Tourbillon remontoire chronometer (for details of this escapement see *The Marine Chronometer* by Rupert Gould, London 1923, p. 146 and fig. 44). There are representations of four different buildings, namely the Walter Scott monument, a Bishop's palace, Rotherham Cathedral and Lichfield Cathedral.

The clock by H. C. Pike is of particular interest, however, since it not only goes but also strikes for 400 days, a rarity indeed.

It will be noticed that in the clocks by James Edwards a feature has been made of the wheelwork. The wheels consist of gear cut rim of brass with a solid cut-glass centre. The dials and pendulum bobs, which are shaped as balls, are also of cut-glass. If I read the description of the clock by R. D. Feltham correctly then it has a compound pendulum, presumably to achieve

The minute hand is a sliding fit on the end of the centre arbor and the gearing down of the hour hand is achieved as follows: behind the central sun wheel of 66 teeth, and concentric with it, is the hour wheel of the same diameter but with 72 teeth, this being free to revolve. The pinion on the driving arm engages both the fixed sun wheel and the movable hour wheel such that the hour wheel is impelled to move forward six additional teeth at each revolution of the arm, i.e., every hour. Since six teeth is one-twelfth of 72, the hour wheel will thus revolve every 12 hours.

H. 10 in (25.4 cm).

William Strutt

William Strutt lived from 1756 to 1830 and so is not strictly within the compass of this book, however many copies of his clock were to be made later by D. Bagshaw of London. This clock is anonymous but can nevertheless be dated to the middle of the nineteenth century.

124 *Skeleton Clock, a Modern Reproduction of a Victorian Clock*

See colour plate XIII

This underlines the point made, that there are some very good reproductions of skeleton clocks that have been made in recent times. There has been no attempt to deceive with this clock and at the moment the dial is the feature that betrays its lack of age – but this could easily be remedied by a faker.

The maker has chosen a simple and elegant design to copy. He has reduced the work that has had to be put into the clock by choosing a one at the hour striking version, otherwise known as passing strike. Here a cam lifts the striking hammer at each hour and one blow is struck on the bell at the top of the clock.

The pendulum controlled clock has a recoil anchor escapement.

H. 12 in (30.5 cm).

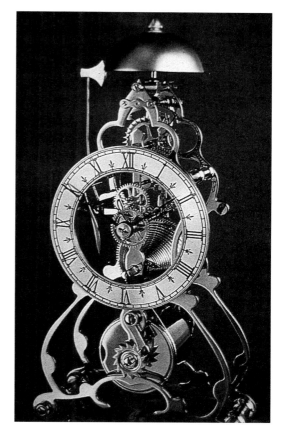

124

125 *Sir Walter Scott Memorial Clock*

by W.F. Evans, *c.* 1870

Scott's Memorial in Edinburgh is one of the famous sights of the city. This clock was designed by William Frederick Evans of Birmingham about 1850 and shown at the Great Exhibition of 1851. When the exhibition ended it was presented to the retiring postmaster at Handsworth but when he died Evans was able to purchase the clock. A direct descendant of Evans, his great-great-grand-daughter presented the clock to The City Museum and Art Gallery in Birmingham where it is now on display to the public.

The version shown here is not the original but one of Evans' many copies for as far as we know he was the only maker to produce this particular clock.

It is 8-day with a fusee. The original had a large platform with a lever escapement and indeed this version has a balance and a lever escapement (fig. 125a), but subsequent versions mostly had pendulums.

The skeletonised chapter ring has Gothic numerals and the blued steel hands are of fleur-de-lis pattern.

The Evans factory produced a number of other skeleton designs, one he made in 1860 even had a detent escapement.

H. 20 in (51 cm).

W. F. Evans

The Soho clock factory was, according to William Frederick Evans' visiting card, established in 1805 and was at Soho Street, Handsworth near Birmingham. W.F. Evans was to become owner of this factory but cannot have been at this date since he was not then born. When he died in 1899 at the age of 81 his son of the same name returned from America to take over the business. In the obituary of this son the firm was described as one of the best-known firms of clockmakers in the United Kingdom, 'which boasts of an existence of over a century and have secured a world-wide reputation having supplied clocks to towns in Australia, United States of America, Canada, India, South Africa, etc.' The business eventually closed in 1935.

The Evans factory made every type of clock and must have been go-ahead since they were one of the first to use the 'Harrington Patent Tubes' in long-case clocks. These were the tubular gongs invented by Harrington in 1885.

Fig. 125a

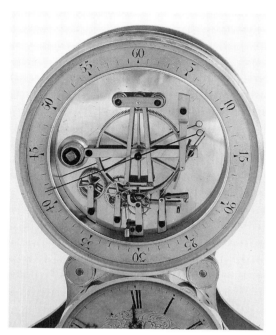

Fig. 126a

126 *Timepiece with Constant Force Escapement*

by Edward Funnel of Brighton, *c.* 1860

See colour plate XIV

The clock has a heavy A frame standing on two plinths, these are then on a black marble base which in turn stands on a further brass base with foliate bracket feet.

There are two dials, one above the other, the lower showing the hours and minutes, the upper showing the seconds. Within this centre seconds dial is displayed the constant force escapement (fig. 126a) which is a chronometer type with a weighted arm to provide the motive force. As this arm drops it releases the fly which can be seen on the right-hand side. This allows the train to run which then recocks the weighted arm.

Surprisingly, the numerals have been painted on the dials as can be seen since the 10 and 11 have virtually disappeared! The hands are of

blued steel and of Gothic pattern. The fine grid-iron pendulum has a thermometer in its bob (fig. 126b) and stands in a trough which prevents damage should the pendulum for any reason achieve too great an amplitude.

All of the brasswork is gilded.

H. 18½ in (47 cm).

Courtesy of the Trustees of the British Museum.

Fig. 126b

127 *Skeleton Clock*

Anonymous, English, *c.* 1850

The plates are skeletonised so as to represent a cathedral with twin crocheted spires. There are seven pillars.

The silvered chapter ring is pierced and has Gothic numerals. The blued steel hands are also of Gothic style.

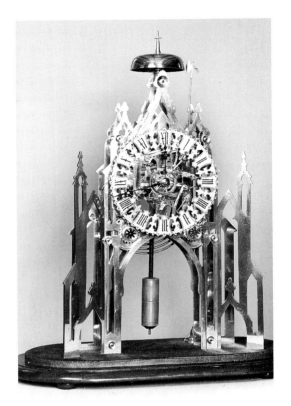

127

128 Chiming Skeleton Clock in the form of York Minster Cathedral

probably by Smith & Sons of Clerkenwell, *c*. 1850

The plates of this clock are elaborately pierced in the form of York Minster Cathedral.

The dial is pierced and silvered with the Gothic numerals on cartouches.

The movement has triple chain-fusees and chimes on eight bells.

There is a moulded brass base to the clock which stands on a further marble base with bun feet.

H. 23 in (58 cm).

There are similar examples in F.B. Royer-Collard, *Skeleton Clocks*, 1969, pp. 5, 32.

These clocks were top of the range and cost £25 upwards – a great deal of money at this time.

The movement stands on a stepped plinth and a marble base with bun feet.

There are twin chain-fusees, hour striking and repeating on a single bell at the top of the clock.

The escapement is dead beat and the compensation pendulum is a wood rod/lead bob combination. Note the unusual type of bob for a skeleton clock.

H. 17½ in (44.5 cm).

128

129

Fig. 129a

129 *Musical Skeleton Clock*

by Ross, *c.* 1860

This clock stands on an ebonised base with bun feet.

The construction is two tier, the lower section containing the twin chain-fusees and the main part of the mechanism. This part has turned-corner pillars with turned finials. The top section, which is supported by four scrolls, carries the dial, which is skeletonised and has Arabic numerals. In the part of this top tier that is beneath the dial is a bar balance which is maintained by a dead-beat escapement in the lower section of the clock.

Above the dial is a double copula.

At the rear of the lower part of the movement are twin pin barrels which can play no less than 15 tunes, one of which is let off at the hour (see fig. 129a).

There are sixteen bells played by two sets of hammers (one set is muted). There is a manual control for the tunes which are named on a silvered ring on the lower tier which also carries the inscription *Ross Fecit*.

A most unusual and elegant design with no expense spared in its construction. The inclusion of two pin barrels is most unusual.

W. of base 18 in (46 cm).

130 *Eight-Day Skeleton Timepiece*

by William Smith of Musselburgh, *c.* 1850

The motive power of this most unusual clock is a helical spring initially made of vulcanised rubber, now made of steel, the original no doubt having perished long ago! In John Smith's *Old Scottish Clockmakers* one reads:

Description and drawing of a timepiece moved by a spring of Vulcanised Caoutchouc, read at a meeting of the Society of Arts held at Edinburgh, 30th of April 1849, by William Smith, Musselburgh, for which the Society's Silver Medal, value five sovereigns, was awarded. The author states that he conceives the superiority of this spring to consist in its perfect invariability from the absence of friction, and simplicity of its application, being in the form of a ring, one end of which is passed through a piece of steel with an eye, to which is attached a hook conecting it with a pulley, both ends being fixed at the bottom of the column by a steel pin passed over them.

The clock stands on a round wooden base with bun feet. A pierced Corinthian column encloses the helical spring, this column having a square base supported by a second square base with a moulded top. On the column capital is the movement with its fusee just above 6 o'clock and with a dead-beat escapement. The fusee is provided with a chain. The clock is pendulum controlled, it would, I think, have made more sense if the clock had been balance controlled. The pendulum bob is just visible behind the helical spring.

Measurements not available.

Mr Smith is, of course, quite correct about the superior qualities of the helical spring. With no intercoil friction the performance of the spring will not alter long term, always providing of course that the stresses the spring is subjected to are kept well within the elastic limit of the material from which the spring is made. Without the modifying influence of friction the output of the spring will be directly proportional to its extention so that the fusee will appear to be unusually steep.

131 'One at the hour' Striking Skeleton Clock

by Morgan of Manchester

The thick frames of this clock are delicately fretted to resemble fuchsias, and supported by four turned feet. The movement stands on a thick marble base with matching marble bun feet.

130

131

A chain-fusee with, unusually in English work, a large great wheel. A silvered dial with Roman numerals and despite the skeletonising, which incidentally is beautifully done, the blued steel hands stand out clearly. The striking hammer is raised once each hour by the motion work, and on falling hits the bell right at the top of the movement. This simple type of clock lends itself to the most elegant of designs, as represented by this particular example.

H. 23 in (58 cm).

132 *Eight-Day Chiming Skeleton Clock*

Anonymous

A three-train skeleton clock chiming the quarters on four bells, one of which is mounted horizontally, the other three vertically. A fifth bell, the hour bell, is the topmost. There are three chain-fusees with maintaining power on the going fusee. All the wheels have six crossings except for the escape wheel which has five. A Brocot escapement with jewelled pins is an unusual inclusion in an English clock (fig. 132b).

The pierced dial has Roman numerals. The hands are of blued steel and of spade design.

The base is rectangular with rounded ends, ebonised and covered in velvet.

Scrolling plates stand on four turned feet.

Note the florets screwed to the front end of the barrel arbors, these prevent the winding key being put onto these squares in error instead of on the fusee arbors which are at IX o'clock, III o'clock and just below the hour wheel. Note also the unusual bob to the pendulum, this being of cylindrical form (fig. 132a).

132

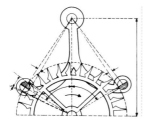

Fig. 132b

Fig. 132a

133 *Skeleton Clock*

by John Pace, Bury St Edmunds, *c.* 1840

The wooden base with its ball feet supports an oval brass base with a heavy chamfer.

The pierced dial has Arabic numerals and blued steel moon hands.

The mechanism has a solid back plate with two scroll feet. The barrel, the chain-fusee and the centre wheel are beneath a shield-shaped bridge, the third wheel, the escape wheel and the pallets have cocks. The clock has an anchor escapement and a short pendulum.

H. 9¼ in (23.5 cm).

John Pace was born in London in 1793 and worked in Bury St Edmunds. He appears in the Poor Rate Assessments volumes for the parish of St James, Bury St Edmunds for the first time in 1824 and up to and including 1868, although he died in 1867.

In 1853 a newspaper published a rhyme which went as follows:

> A Silversmith is Mr. Pace
> He makes new clocks, old ones, new face
> Guards, Broaches, Pins and other things
> Ah, yes 'and sells new wedding rings'.

133

This makes it sound as if Mr Pace was purely a retailer, but then he produced a skeleton clock for the Great Exhibition of 1851 which went for three years on one winding and they were keen to record the true makers of the items shown.

Also see the note about the year clock (no. 134) by Pace below.

134 *A Year-Going Skeleton Timepiece with Calendar and State of Wind Indicator*

by John Pace, Bury St Edmunds, *c.* 1850
See col. plate XV

The chamfered and arched C scroll plates have five pillars and the whole is raised on two concave pillars on a brass oval base plate. Beneath this is an ebonised wooden base. On top of the base is a spirit level and a beat plate. On the front of the top part of the base is *John Pace* and on the next level down is *Bury St. Edmunds*.

There are three gilt dials, the first at the top a skeletonised chapter ring with Arabic numerals with blued steel serpentine hands and the other two are interlinked dials below. That on the left is the calendar dial and that on the right is the up-and-down dial showing the reserve in weeks from 52 downwards.

The movement has two chain-fusees connected to four spring barrels. There is a high count six-wheel train and a dead-beat escapement. The pendulum is plain and uncompensated. The upper part of the train has typical Pace design cocks.

H. 19 in (48 cm), W. 14¼ in (36 cm).

This is one of only four or five year clocks known by these makers, for these clocks are really the work of two people. It would seem that Pace was the designer whereas Benjamin Parker, a gunsmith by trade, was the clockmaker. Similar clocks are known bearing both names and others with just Parker's name.

135 *Prince Albert Edward and Princess Alexandra Skeleton Timepiece*

Anonymous, 1863

This clock normally stands on an oval ebonised base but this has been removed.

The scrolled plates are surmounted by the Prince of Wales feathers.

The chapter ring is pierced and has red numerals on circular cartouches. The minutes are marked on a ring surrounding these chapters. The chapter ring is also surmounted by Prince of Wales feathers incorporating the emblem of the three kingdoms and Wales. Below the VI is the monogram *AA* (Albert–Alexandra).

The movement has a chain-fusee, an anchor escapement and a pendulum.

H. 12½ in (32 cm).

This clock was reputedly made to celebrate the marriage of Prince Albert Edward, later King Edward VII, to Princess Alexandra of Denmark in 1863.

135

9 Time Signals and Electric Clocks

*E*arly in the nineteenth century two important things occurred: one was the growth of the railway system and the other was the development of the electric telegraph. At this time each town kept its own local time, which meant that as a train travelled, say, from London to Plymouth there was a difference of approximately 16 minutes between the two local times. To begin with this must have caused consternation to those people wearing a watch who found that it was unaccountably wrong when they left the train. Not only that but it became very difficult to work out a timetable and a tricky problem for a train driver to check whether he was keeping to it.

A picture of Tom Tower and the Great Clock at Christchurch, Oxford, shows that in about 1860 it had two minute hands. One of these showed Greenwich time and the other the local time in Oxford. That showing Oxford time had a counterpoised hand and pointed to 1.30 and the other indicated 1.25.

There was obviously a need for standard time throughout the country and when this became available the electric telegraph provided a means of disseminating it.

In the section on Electric Clocks below, pp. 157–63, the details of the Greenwich Clocks that provided this standard time will be found and in fig. (xi) some of these clocks may be seen. On the left is inset a picture of Airy's transit instrument which is effectively a fixed telescope mounted so that it can only swing absolutely vertically in the north to south plane. It used to sight on to one particular star which of course will be higher in the sky at one time of the year than another. For time-telling purposes the star is that which passes directly overhead at midnight, which is

Fig. (x) Portable transit instrument

sidereal time and the clock that shows sidereal time can be seen in front of the observer. Since the exact difference between sidereal time and mean solar time is known it is then possible to compute the latter, this being the time used in everyday life.

In fact in the photograph the observer is using the transit instrument to observe our own star, the sun.

Fig. (x) shows a portable transit instrument; a full description of this and the setting and use of these instruments is given in the 16th edition of Britten's *Watch and Clock Maker's Handbook,* London, 1976 on p. 323 and 324. This edition was revised by the author of this book.

The telescope to the right of the transit instrument shown in fig. (xi) was that known as the. S. E. Equatorial and is in use with a spectroscope.

Next to this is the Gate Clock by Shepherd situated at the entrance to the Observatory. Although this clock shows 8 hours 57 minutes in the photograph (which was taken in 1870) this is not civil time. This is because it is showing astronomer's time and at that period the astronomer's day started at 12 noon. To make things even more complicated seamen also started their day at noon instead of midnight

Fig. (xi)

but at twelve hours before the start of the civil day so that they were 24 hours ahead of the astronomers. Thus noon of the 1st of January for a sailor was noon of the 31st December by civil timekeeping and according to the astronomers the 1st of January did not start until noon on the 1st by civil reckoning!

Above this picture of the gate clock is a view of the Observatory itself, the building was designed by Christopher Wren. Rising above the chimneys is the time ball more of which will be said later. Rearing skywards to the left of the time ball is the anemometer for reading the wind speed. In the bottom right corner of fig. (xi) is Shepherd's master clock. To the right of the clock in the round case is the control for getting the clock to time. Below this is the apparatus for operating the time ball. Lastly, top right, is the chronograph by Dent used for recording the observations. Since continuous motion is required for the chronograph drum its speed of rotation is controlled by a conical pendulum which, instead of moving from side to side, rotates about its suspension so that the bob has a circular motion. The operative in the picture is reading the previous night's observations.

Royal Observatory drawings, dated 1856, show the chronograph in complete detail. The chronograph is still at the National Maritime Museum but various bits of it have gone astray.

Shepherd's clocks were installed in 1852 and controlled, by 'galvanism' through the telegraph system, various clocks and time balls of which details will be given in due course. Thus 'Greenwich Time', or 'railway' time as it was called, began to be distributed throughout Great Britain.

It soon became evident that time had to be standardised throughout the world, not just in one country, and in 1884 there was a conference in Washington when it was agreed in the face of strenuous opposition from France that the meridian passing through the centre of the transit instrument in Greenwich should be chosen as the 'Prime Meridian' of the world – in other words zero longitude. On this was based the International Time Zone system.

The French, in fact, stood little chance in getting their way in having the Prime Meridian pass through Paris, which was their wish, since nearly three-quarters of the world's shipping already had the meridian of

Greenwich on their charts. Furthermore, the vast American network of railways used a time zone system based on Greenwich mean time. One other country failed to ratify the agreement, Ireland, which stubbornly refused to accept the inevitable until 1916, keeping Dublin time instead.

France eventually turned over to Greenwich time on 30 June 1911 when at midnight the dial-less clock of the Eiffel Tower flashed Greenwich time across the city. It was remarked in the *H.J.* for July 1911 that France is the land of clocks, but there is no uniformity about them, and even the electric clocks at all the cross streets seem to find a way of disagreeing among themselves. 'The 9 minutes that we shall have to live twice over,' writes a Paris correspondent, 'will not make much difference to any of us, but it will be highly agreeable if the same tale be told in all the quarters of the city.' The difference between the local time of Paris and London is actually 9 minutes and 21 seconds and the Paris clocks had to be put back this amount to standardise the two times.

Although Big Ben was never controlled by Greenwich its time of striking was relayed to Greenwich so that a record could be kept of its performance.

The electric telegraph proved useful in other ways, the speed at which messages were transmitted being one of them. In 1848 the Victorian public learned of this speed in a most dramatic way. Part of the Great Western Railway had been opened and trains were running from Paddington to Slough. Also along its lines ran the newly invented electric telegraph. On the 1st of January a murderer named Tawell was arrested in London, his presence on the train from Slough being notified by a telegraph message which passed him as he was on his journey. Somewhat after this handbills were distributed by the telegraph company. 'The electric fluid', said one of them, 'travels at the rate of 280,000 miles a second. By its powerful agency murderers have been apprehended (as in the case of the late Tawell), thieves detected and lastly, which is of no little importance, the timely assistance of medical aid has been procured in cases which would otherwise have proved fatal.' These handbills were reproduced in *The Telegraphic Journal*, Vol. 4, pp. 170–1, 1876.

The figure for the speed at which electricity travelled was that determined by Charles Wheatstone, whom we shall meet in the section on Electric Clocks. He obtained it by a most ingenious experiment which obviously had its defects but was nevertheless the first one that stood any chance of success. Considering the difficulties in making such a measurement it is not a result to be sneered at. Wheatstone conducted his experiment in 1834 and the results were published in Vol. 124 of the *Philosophical Transactions* of 1834, p. 583.

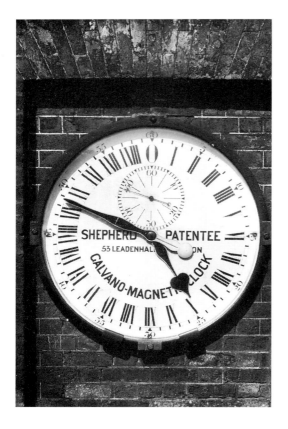

Charles Shepherd was at 53 Leadenhall St., in the City of London from 1845 to 1864, from 1867–1875 the title becomes '& Son'. He lived at Hendon, where he was sponsored by a wealthy resident, J.F. Pawson, who first installed Shepherd's clock system in his firm's warehouses.

Shepherd exhibited in the Great Exhibition of 1851 and his clock dial was given a position of prominence. An illustration of this and also a report on the clock was published in the *Illustrated London News*. In 1862 Shepherd received an Honourable Mention. In the International Inventions Exhibition of 1885 he received a Bronze Medal.

He took out a patent (No. 12567) for electric clocks in 1849 and another for an electrical turret clock in 1881 (No. 3696). A turret clock made to this patent is described in *A.H.*, Autumn 1977 pp. 460–3. No obituary can be found in the pages of the *H.J.* so that one of the most important figures in nineteenth century horology died unsung.

Fig. (xii) A close up of the gate clock with its 24-hour dial, unusual in going from 1 to 24 in Roman numerals. This spoils the appearance; there is no balance on either side of the upper half with all the heavy numerals on the left side of the dial.

Note the large poising weight to the minute hand disguised somewhat by being painted white so that it does not show up too clearly. The dial is inscribed *SHEPHERD PATENTEE 53 LEADENHALL ST. LONDON. GALVANO – MAGNETIC CLOCK.*

136 *The Greenwich Time Ball*

This time ball is 5 ft (152 cm) in diameter and is mounted on top of the Octagon Room at the Greenwich Observatory. It was the brain-child of a Captain Wanchope R.N., and was first erected in 1833. However it was not until 1852 that it was discharged by means of an electrical signal from the Shepherd Clock. Although in theory it could be made to fall at every hour it is in fact operated once a day, and I say 'is' deliberately since it still falls at the time of one o'clock (mean solar time) to this day. The mast on which the ball is mounted is of square section with a groove on one side. The ball, which was then black but is now red, rests on the top of a slider which runs in the groove. When the time ball was first installed it was manually operated, but before long the ball was released by an electric signal from the Shepherd master clock. When the ball first starts to fall it does so very rapidly but a piston attached to it soon enters an open-topped iron cylinder.

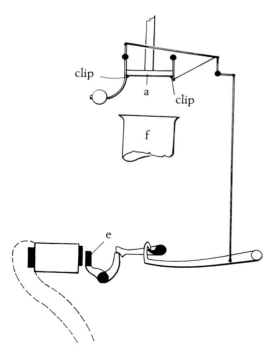

136

The air in this cylinder can only escape slowly through a small hole in its base so that it acts on the ball as a pneumatic brake. 1 o'clock is indicated at the instant at which the ball separates from the cross above it. So accurate is the mechanism that the error in letting off the ball seldom exceeds three-tenths of a second. The cross incidentally denotes the cardinal points of the compass (these are shown in fig. 137).

This ball could be seen falling from the ships in the Thames Basin so that their chronometers could be set or rated.

In 1855 in December the ball was blown down, and probably damaged since during the nineteenth century it was made of wood and canvas. It was replaced by an aluminium ball in 1919. High winds and snow can prevent the raising of the ball but apart from during the Second World War and for some years during the 1950s the ball has dropped every day at one o'clock since 1833.

137 *The Deal Time Ball*

There is another time ball – still in position and still in use – at Deal. It looks very like the one at Greenwich but is on its own in the 'The Old Semaphore Tower', the tower being used for semaphore-telegraph until it was fitted up with the time ball. It is a square building some 40 ft (12.2 m) in height, close to the beach and about 200 yd (183 m) south of the pier. This time ball was sponsored by Sir George B. Airy in 1853 and brought into use in 1855 when it continued to be used until 1927. The ball, as with that at Greenwich, is dropped at one o'clock. A magnificent drawing has been prepared of the mechanism by David Penney which is published here by kind permission of the Dover Museum.

A check was made on the accuracy of the time ball at Deal since a signal operated by the fall of the ball was sent back to Greenwich.

Time balls in Operation in 1861 This is part of a list compiled by G.B. Airy with the entries referring to time balls abroad and proposed time balls omitted.

Both the Greenwich and the Deal time balls have already been mentioned.

There was a time ball at The Electrical and International Telegraph Companies office in the Strand (see fig. (xiii)). This was put into service in 1852. The ball was 5 ft (152 cm) in diameter, made of zinc, painted black with a wide white band around its middle and topped by a weather vane with *ETC* upon it. There was another at the 'City Observatory' in other words French of Cornhill, (see p. 97). Yet another was at Dent's corner shop at 33 and 34, Cockspur St., Charing Cross. This is illustrated in Vaudrey Mercer's book on Dent p. 545. All of these time balls were dropped by signals from the Royal Greenwich Observatory.

There was a time ball on the Victoria Tower Liverpool, this however was controlled by a signal from the Liverpool Observatory.

Another time ball was dropped by a galvanic signal at the Royal Observatory at Edinburgh.

A time ball at Portsmouth Royal Naval College was dropped by hand.

Another time ball is known to have been at Glasgow in 1859 but no particulars could be found.

In the section on Exhibitions there will be found details of a time ball erected by John Bennett. This time ball capped his display at the 1862 Exhibition. It fell each hour as this was a facility available from Greenwich.

Time-guns Another interesting way of disseminating time was by letting off a gun which could be done automatically by means of an electric signal just as easily as dropping a time ball. Time-guns were, of course, not designed to give accurate time over any appreciable distance

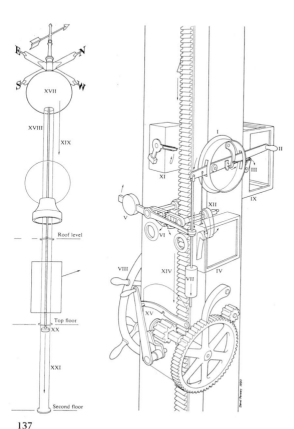

The key to the figure of the Deal Time Ball and its mechanism

 I is the lever cover.
 II is the lever.
 III is the arm by which the magnets release it.
 IV is the switch.
 V is the compensating weight to work the toothed segments VI.
 VII is the weight-moving lever.
 VIII is the wheel for winding up the ball.
 IX the magnets.
 X not shown.
 XI is the tapper.
 XII shows the shaft and the hooks for holding it which are worked by the toothed segments VI.
 XIII is the copper disc acted on by the knob of the shaft and which releases the arm of the switch at the proper time to send it to the normal position.
 XIV is the rack and pinion for raising the shaft.
 XV is the lever for taking the pinion out of mesh with the rack.
 XVI not shown.
 XVII is the ball which is hollow and constructed of wood covered in zinc and painted black. It is 15 ft (4.6 m) in circumference, in other words roughly the same size as the Greenwich ball.
 XVIII is the 2½ in (6.4 cm) square wooden shaft that supports the ball. The rise and fall of the ball is about 12 ft (3.7 m). The ball comes to rest on an india-rubber cushion on top of the platform.
 XIX shows the direction in which the ball falls and also to be seen is its position when it comes to rest.
 XX is a plunger fixed to the bottom of the shaft. It is about 8 in (20 cm) in diameter and fits into an iron cylinder, (XXI). The inside of this cylinder is kept greased. The plunger has a hole to allow air to escape and the whole acts as explained above.

Fig. (xiii)

because of the uncertainty of the speed of travel of the sound. One could not just make an allowance for the distance one was away from the gun since the strength and direction of the wind also came into the equation. Soon after the time ball was erected in Deal a time-gun was installed at Dover Castle, this being fired at noon by a current from Greenwich.

In 1861 there were two time-guns in Edinburgh, one on Carlton Hill and the other set up that year at Edinburgh Castle. In 1863 time-guns were established in the Old Norman keep at Newcastle and at North Shields.

Other Services Until 1870 the telegraph companies were privately owned but in that year they were taken over by the state and the Post Office took over the contracts then in force. Subscribers were charged on a sliding scale depending on the signals they received and the distance they were from the G.P.O. at St Martin's le Grand. Subscribers had to supply their own

terminal equipment, one example being the time ball at the City Observatory (see above) which was on the roof of French's shop in Cornhill.

Other terminals might be small time balls in shop windows, galvanometers or bells or any combination of these. One unusual example was erected outside the premises of the hatter George Carter of 211–217, Old Kent Rd. in South East London. It was the bust of a gentleman wearing a top hat. At just before 1 o'clock the hat was raised and at precisely 1 o'clock the hat fell back onto the head. After the First World War the top hat was changed for a bowler.

Electric Clocks

The discovery of the Leyden jar by Musschenbroek and his pupil Cuncus was made in about 1745 and allowed electricity to be stored in such a way that for the first time some use could be made of it. However it was not until 1800 that Alessandro Volta demonstrated that electricity could be generated by immersing two suitable metals in a salty fluid. From his experiments came the famous Volta's pile, the first practical source of current electricity. He invented another type of battery called the 'Crown of Cups'.

Shortly after this, in 1802 Romagnosi of Trente found that a wire carrying an electric current caused a compass needle to move. However his findings were not published and it was not until 1819 that Professor Hans Christian Oerstedt rediscovered the effect; this discovery was made almost by accident. Andre M. Ampere then discovered the solenoid, a helical coil of wire which acts like a bar magnet when a current passes through it.

Both Humphrey Davy and Dominique Arago independently found that the solenoid's magnetic field could be considerably increased by wrapping the wire around a soft iron bar; when current ceases to flow the soft iron loses its magnetism.

These effects could not be displayed for very long, the primitive cells in use at the time were simply not up to it and it was not until 1838 that Daniel invented his cell that was able for the first time to produce a reliable and steady current.

Thus a year after Victoria came to the throne everything was in place for electrical horology to come on to the scene.

It was in fact in Scotland that the first really successful electric clock was made and it was the brain-child of Alexander Bain.

At the age of nineteen Bain attended a lecture at Thurso on light, heat and electricity. This was in 1830 and at this time Bain was apprenticed to Mr Seller, a watchmaker of Wick in Scotland. This lecture proved to be a turning point in Bain's life for he was fascinated by what he heard. In 1837 he moved to London, an excellent mechanic and with some knowledge of electricity. He worked in Clerkenwell as a journeyman clockmaker and devoted his leisure to study. In Bain's own words quoted in a book written by John Finlaison which was published in 1843:

> As soon as I obtained employment, I devoted all my leisure to my favourite study, and attended lectures at the Adelaide Gallery and the Polytechnic Institution; and seeing the beautiful electro-magnetic machines in action at those places, first drew my attention to how they could be applied to useful purposes. The application of this mysterious power to the mechanism of my own business was naturally the first to suggest itself; afterwards I thought on many methods of applying it to telegraphs; and, among other methods which occurred to me was that of printing the intelligence, instead of showing it by signs, which I knew had been done before. I therefore confined my exertions to the electric clocks and electric printing telegraph; and by July, 1840, I had so far matured both these inventions that I was desirous of meeting with some party who would assist me the means of bringing them into operation.

In fact he went to see Professor Wheatstone, of King's College, on 1 August 1840.

The rights and wrongs of what followed are difficult to determine but the upshot was that Wheatstone exhibited an electric clock to the Royal Society of London on 26 November 1840 – but Bain and John Barwise had applied for a British Patent on the previous 10 October.

The validity of this patent enabled Barwise to successfully serve an injunction against Wheatstone to stop him exhibiting the clock in the Adelaide Gallery as his own invention. Soon after that Bain's clock was put on public exhibition in the Polytechnic Institution. The patent mentioned is No. 8783. The patent was granted on 11 January 1841. Bain then was the first to maintain a clock pendulum by electromagnetic impulses.

The Bain clock, the method of making contact
A slider that is operated by the pendulum runs in a block that has in one position gold contacts. When the slider is moved by the pendulum it makes contact with the gold inlay and current flows. It flows through a coil that actually forms the pendulum bob and this is energised. Since the coil passes over weak permanent magnets a mutual attraction occurs which is just sufficient to maintain the oscillations of the pendulum. Bain's choice of gold for the contact and silver for the slider was inspired. Although rather soft gold is free from oxidation problems and has a low electrical resistance. This latter characteristic is important in a circuit whose losses must be kept to a minimum.

There are two of Bain's clocks in the Royal Scottish Museum, one which is thought to be his No. '0', his original clock. Both are quite reliable although they are not now driven by an earth battery as were the originals but by one-and-a-half volt Leclanche cells.

There is another Bain clock in the National Maritime Museum. When I was first working there this was without its contact block and slider; I was privileged to be commissioned to make a replacement for it so that the clock could be got working. This I did and in fact it was surprisingly easy to do. To ensure that the new parts would never be mistaken for the originals the new block was made of a plastic material.

138 *Electric Wall Clock*
attributed to Henry Kerr, *c.* 1860

This electric clock is based closely on the system used by Bain where the contact is made by a slider operated by the pendulum. When the current from the battery flows the coil that constitutes the bob of the pendulum is energised producing a weak electromagnetic field. It is the interaction between this field and that from the permanent magnets over which the coil runs that results in impulse being given.

The case of the clock is mahogany. It has glazed front and side panels, turned corner pillars and carved foliate cresting. The chapter ring is black glass with reverse painted white Roman numerals. The centre of the dial is open so that the skeletonised mechanism with its lyre pattern plates can be seen. It has a centre seconds hand and moon pattern hour and minute hands.

The pendulum has a second large bob, which is spherical in shape, whose position can be adjusted micrometrically. This is needed for rating purposes. The position of the coil cannot be changed as it is fixed by the fact that the magnets must remain at its centre, so it is not possible to move this to bring the clock to time.

Measurements not available.

Courtesy Deryk Roberts.

Battery Cell Development I have already mentioned an earth battery and had better perhaps explain that if two metal plates such as zinc and copper (or indeed zinc and carbon) are put into damp earth then about one volt will be generated. These batteries are known as corrosion batteries since the zinc is slowly eaten away. During a dry spell the earth must be watered. By making the plates big enough the effects of polarisation could be minimised.

The reason for the use of earth batteries was that at the time these early clocks were introduced the other cells available all had some defect or other. However it was not long before an important advance was made, namely the development of the Leclanche cell. This cell had an immediate and long-lasting popularity and during the rest of the period we are interested in was used widely on the railways and for telegraph and telephone services. The chief disadvantage of the Leclanche cell was its lack of portability. In the late 1880s several inventors were experimenting with dry versions and by 1890 commercial manufacture of these began.

I have mentioned the use of gold and silver for contacts but there was a third in use, this was platinum. Platinum became of interest in the middle of the eighteenth century when it was known only in the form of small granules, the state in which it was found in nature. Attempts to melt these grains failed because of the high melting point of platinum which is 3,080°F (1,693°C). At the end of the eighteenth century William H. Wollaston discovered that larger, malleable pieces of platinum could be made by pressing the powdered metal into blocks, heating them in a coke furnace, and striking them while

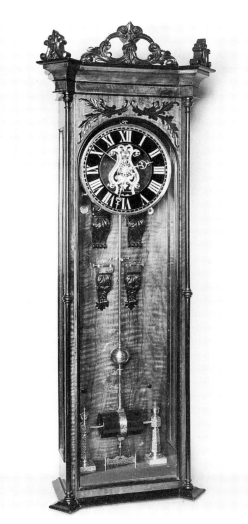

138

they were hot with a heavy hammer. Platinum was not always an expensive material, it was, in fact, used in Russia at one time as low value coinage! At the start its use was very limited but it is of interest to note that there is a marine chronometer in the collections of the British Museum made by John Arnold & Son in 1790 which has platinum as one of the metals in its bimetallic balance, the earliest use in horology that I can find.

Dr Matheus Hipp of Neuchatel, working independently at the same time as Bain also devised a system that was very popular. What was unique about his design was that it was impulse on demand. When the swing of the pendulum dropped to a predetermined figure, contact was made and impulse given. Although Hipp was a Swiss his design was so good and copied without shame so many times by English makers that it will have to be described in due course (see pp. 161–2).

Shepherd's Mean Solar Standard Clock at Greenwich The next man to come on to the scene was Charles Shepherd. He was responsible for what is perhaps the best known electric clock in the world. It was installed in the Old Royal Observatory in Greenwich and controlled the famous gate clock, for the use of the public, and four other clocks within the building. Additionally it controlled a clock in the Observatory belonging to the Royal Hospital School, the necessary connecting wires for this passing under the ground of Greenwich Park. It also actuated time balls, as discussed earlier and signals also went to London Bridge Station.

The clock system was installed in 1852. In 1866 time signals were sent to *The Great Eastern* during the laying of the Atlantic cable and then in October, after its completion, to Harvard University. It was not to be superseded until 1893, a quite remarkable fact in this era of rapid advances, the clock that took its place being Dent No. 2012.

Shepherd's clock had an electric gravity escapement and was the first of this kind to be made. It was patented in 1849, the patent number being 12567. A small gravity arm is released by the pendulum and in falling gives impulse to the pendulum. The arm is then lifted

by electrical means to be latched awaiting its next release. Fig. (xiv) shows Shepherd's clock in position in Greenwich Observatory. The explanations of its working can be found in Hope-Jones 1950.

One of the snags with this clock and in fact with many others of this period was that the pendulum itself had to make the contact thus interfering with its free swing. Although better examples were soon to be produced, for instance by Sir David Gill in 1880, it was not until 1895 that F. Hope-Jones and G.B. Bowell together produced the answer to all the problems associated with driving electric clocks that were both accurate and reliable. This answer was the clock to be marketed as the Synchronome and will be discussed later.

However, to return to the Shepherd clock, a lecture was given on the Greenwich system of time signals by William Ellis on 24 February 1865

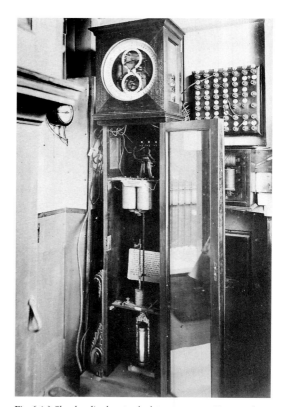

Fig. (xiv) Shepherd's electric clock in position at Greenwich.

which was reproduced in the *H.J.* issue of 1 April 1865. On pp. 86–91 the Shepherd clock and two methods of correcting its errors are described.

Shepherd's clock became known as the Mean Solar Standard Clock, its opposite number was a Sidereal Standard Clock. The errors of this latter clock was determined astronomically and at least once a day the two clocks were compared and the mean time clock corrected. This correction was done without the need to touch the hands; an important feature of the Shepherd clock.

The methods of doing this are interesting: I say methods since the first had been superseded by 1865. Initially an auxiliary pendulum, consisting of a long wire with a brass cup weighted with shot as its bob hung by the side of the master clock. This pendulum could, when correction was needed, be linked to the main pendulum at a point immediately above the neck of its mercurial jar. When the auxiliary pendulum was longer than the clock pendulum it would cause it to go slow. However, a brass fork could be made to slide down the wire so as to shorten the wire and thus make the master pendulum speed up. When the necessary change was accomplished the auxiliary pendulum was disengaged until next required.

The above method was abandoned in 1860 in favour of electromagnetic correction. A permanent magnet was fixed to the pendulum rod and ran above a coil that could be energised so as to either attract or repel the magnet. Turning on the coil for about ten minutes changed the time of the clock by a second.

The Sidereal Standard was a clock by Hardy which in 1854 had electric contacts fitted to it so that sidereal seconds could be transmitted to the Time Desk and to the new barrel chronograph by Dent. This chronograph, also installed in 1854, recorded on a paper chart the seconds from the sidereal clock and the times of the star observations from the transit circle.

In 1869, Airy ordered a new sidereal clock from Dent; No. 1906, with a chronometer-type escapement. By 1873 its sophisticated temperature-compensated pendulum had even been fitted with a barometric corrector. This clock which was housed in a basement, where in any case the temperature varied very little, had an accuracy of a tenth of a second a day.

Hipp's Toggle We now return to Hipp's method of impulsing a pendulum which although devised in 1842 was fundamentally much more sound than any to be developed for a long time after. This is because the method enabled an occasional and powerful contact to be made by the moving pendulum without unduly affecting its time of swing.

In one arrangement the pendulum has its bob above an electro-magnet which is fixed to the case. Also fixed to the case is a block which carries a toggle mounted on a spring blade. It hangs freely and is picked up by a notched piece which is carried by the pendulum. At normal amplitudes the toggle is simply pushed aside at each swing of the pendulum. However as the arc drops eventually the toggle catches in the notch

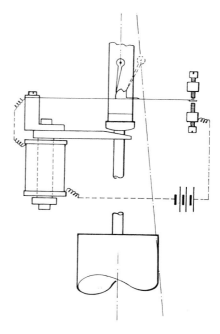

Fig. (xv) Another arrangement of the Hipp impulsing system is shown in this figure, and in this example the armature is not beneath the pendulum but is mounted near the toggle. It is forked so as pass both back and front of the pendulum rod so as to give an even impulse. The pendulum amplitude has to reduce until the trailing finger can only reach the position shown as dotted. As the pendulum moves back to the right the finger will enter the notch and depress the spring that carries the notch causing contact to be made. The soft iron core thus becomes magnetised and the forces between it and the permanent magnet mounted upon the pendulum rod produces an impulse.

and will be pushed up as a result and will close the contacts. With the contacts momentarily closed current will flow through the coil and impulse will be given. The geometry is such that at the exact moment the contacts close the armature is directly beneath the pendulum so that impulse is given at the ideal time, that is when the pendulum is at zero position.

Clocks of this type performed so well that one was actually tried out as an Observatory timekeeper. Dr Hirsch of the Neuchatel Observatory 1884–90 quoted it as having a mean variation in rate of plus or minus 0.03 seconds per day, although this claim must be taken with a pinch of salt! However the performance of these clocks was so good that it took a clock of the calibre of a Rieffler (Howse, 1980, pp. 215–16) to supplant them. Certainly all things being equal they surpassed the best Graham dead-beat escapement clocks.

The Synchronome Clock   The time has now come to describe the Synchronome clock which was the ultimate development in electric clocks in the Victorian era. Like most of the best ideas the concept is simple. The pendulum operates a count wheel which each revolution unlocks the impulse arm. As this falls it impulses the pendulum but when it has finished doing this it continues to fall until a contact mounted on it meets a fixed contact.

The great virtue of this way of making contact is that the whole momentum of the gravity arm is utilised to effect an extremely rapid contact whereupon an equally rapid break occurs as the arm is thrown upwards. We had the very opposite situation with the Shepherd clock where the slowly moving pendulum had to make the contact so that there was a slow make and an equally slow break. As current flows then, a solenoid throws the impulse arm up again until it is once more locked and the cycle is complete. Thus the pendulum has to do no work other than turn the count wheel, and every 30 seconds unlock the impulse arm. It does this at the most favourable time when the pendulum is passing through the dead point. The impulse is constant since it is delivered by a gravity arm.

The clock was of course able to control as many slave clocks as required and was the

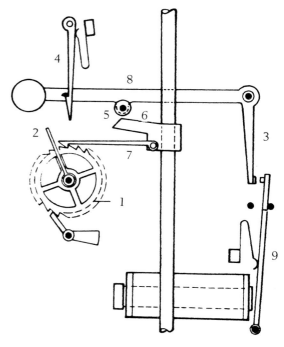

Fig. (xvi) The Synchronome Electric Clock
1 the count wheel, usually revolves in 30 seconds being pulled around by the ratchet **7** which is fixed to the pendulum rod. The trip **2** unlocks the catch **4** which is holding up the weighted arm **8**. This falls and in doing so the roller **5** runs down the impulse arm **6** and gives the pendulum impulse. As it continues to fall the contact **3** on the arm **8** makes the circuit, the armature is energised and the arm **9** hits the arm **8** and throws it back up to where it is once more locked by catch **4**.

favourite master clock for domestic use really until the quartz clock took over and slave clocks became a thing of the past.

Turret Clocks   The winding of Turret clocks can be a great chore (see pp. 165–6) and it was not long before somebody realised the potential that the electric motor had to take it over.

F. Hope-Jones says in his book *Electric Clocks* 'That he suggested that Big Ben should be modified so as to be maintained by means of a Huygens endless chain, electrically rewound. To make good sense the clock should be driven further down the train than the barrel.'

I myself modified a public clock recently in this way and put a bicycle sprocket on the arbor of the wheel before the escape wheel. As the driving weight descends it switches a small motor which then rewinds until switched off again. I will emphasise that the clock I worked on was not changed in any way; all the modifications are reversible and there would be no way of telling that any changes had ever been made. Naturally great care must be taken to label the pieces removed and to store them safely. Incidentally, there was no choice about changing the clock to electric winding as it had to move to a position where there was no possibility of a drop for the weights. That does not mean to say, however, that it may not be moved again to a position where it would be possible to put it back to its original state.

F. Hope-Jones, by the way, was a prophet since in the *Electric Times* of November 1895, then known as *Lighting*, he predicted that the electric clock of the future would be one driven by a small continuously running synchronous motor geared down to make a mantelshelf clock, plugged in to the consumers A.C. supply. However, this advance had to await the universal adoption of alternating current with a controlled and standard frequency. This was certainly nowhere near happening in the Victorian era.

This then is a somewhat superficial look at electricity as used with clockwork. Anyone who would like to pursue this fascinating aspect of clockmaking should start by reading the book already referred to, namely *Electric Clocks* by F. Hope-Jones (London, 1950).

10 Turret Clocks

The Victorian era was without doubt the best possible time for the manufacture of public clocks. Turret clocks (as these large clocks are known in horology) are a different breed to all other types of clock and are usually the province of specialists.

Although all of the basic principles still apply – good gearing, a sound escapement and so on – the methods of construction and the materials used are unlike those of conventional clocks, especially during the Victorian period. The frames are usually of cast iron, and bushed with bronze to form the bearings, which are often removable for ease of cleaning. The escapements used might be the anchor, the dead beat or some constant force type, for instance the gravity escapement. As an alternative to the constant force escapement there might be a remontoire device in the train. These inclusions which guarantee that the same impulsing force arrives at the escapement regardless of what is happening further back in the train are extremely sensible in a turret clock. The force being extracted from the train to drive the hands can vary greatly due to the wind, weather or lack of maintenance. With a constant-force device plenty of extra torque can be provided to allow for these variations without there being any result on the swing of the pendulum, for all of the mechanical turret clocks of this period are pendulum-controlled.

The most famous constant-force escapement is not, unnaturally, that in the Westminster Clock widely known as Big Ben. This escapement, the double three-legged gravity, was invented by Denison, an amateur horologist. These types of constant-force escapements have their roots in Thomas Mudge's work. He designed an escapement in which impulse is given by weighted arms, and once these have dropped and given the pendulum a push, the only function of the escape wheel is to return these arms to their original position. As far as is known Mudge never made an example of his own escapement, the earliest known clock to incorporate his design being one by Catherway in the British Museum. Not all arms rely upon their weight to give the necessary impulse, some are sprung, but this latter type, developed by Hardy, was not used in turret clocks.

Maintaining power becomes particularly important in turret clocks, which by their very nature can take a long time to wind. Without maintaining power, of course, the clock would stop during winding with a serious loss of time being the result if the hands are not reset. It can also be dangerous to some dead-beat escapements for the power to be removed. If there is a solid and unyielding link between the crutch and the heavy swinging pendulum there is the possibility that the pallets will be crushed into the tip of one of the escape wheel teeth and so damage it.

It can take a long time to wind a turret clock, to begin with there will probably be gearing between the winding arbor and the barrel simply to give enough purchase to enable winding to take place. Thus it may take six turns, say of the winding handle to give one turn of the barrel. The barrel in turn may have perhaps 30 turns of cable on it, this is why it can take so long to wind the clock. Although admittedly Big Ben is a somewhat untypical example, during the period from 1859 until 1913, when the clock was wound by hand, it took five hours to wind the striking and chiming trains although the going side only took about 20 minutes. There was no maintaining power on the chiming and striking trains and winding had to be stopped each time the clock was ready to sound. The men winding could not forget to do this since there was an interlock that prevented winding during the active periods of the striking and chiming.

Maintaining power, of course, has to be provided for the going train and this is described as it differs from the normal. Once the going barrel is fully wound it will run the clock for ten days but this is purely a safety measure and the winding of the going side is done once a week. Since 1913 the winding of the other two trains has been done by electric motors and the process still takes 40 minutes three times a week!

Full details of the winding of Big Ben are to be found in Vaudrey Mercer's excellent book, *Edward John Dent and his Successors*, Ticehurst, 1977, pp. 394–8. On p. 395 Mercer says that it took about a month for a man new to the winding to master what has to be done, the consequences of a mistake in the complex process could be disastrous. It is true to say, however, that there is always a need for special skills when clocks have to be wound and this is not always appreciated; many a Museum has discovered this too late. It appears on the face of it to be a simple process but at least one clock in the British Museum has been saved from a major disaster by the quick thinking of the skilled clockmaker who was winding it when the clickwork failed.

Bolt and shutter maintaining power or some variant of this is the usual type found in turret clocks, the only field in which this archaic form of maintaining power is found in the nineteenth century. It has the slight disadvantage that if winding is completed with the maintaining power still in operation, which of course it normally would be, then until it disengages double the normal torque will be applied to the train. I say a slight disadvantage because it takes a long time for the heavy pendulum of a turret clock to react to changes in the power reaching the escapement. Sun and planet maintaining power does not suffer from this defect but on the other hand it does take twice as long to wind the clock when this type is used which may be a disadvantage where smaller clocks are concerned. Another type of maintaining power used is Airy's.

A magnificent turret clock was on display at the 1851 Exhibition, it was made by Dent and bore the inscription *Clockmaker to the Queen*. This was a large clock with a one-and-a-half second pendulum weighing 2 cwt (102 kg), this being of the zinc and steel variety. It had a pin wheel escapement with 40 pins in the wheel which was a mere 4 in (10 cm) in diameter. It had a spring remontoire which was rewound every 30 seconds. The clock wheels were all of cast iron except for the escape wheel. It had bolt and shutter maintaining power, a vital inclusion since there was little drop for the weights and the clock had to be rewound at frequent intervals. During the ten weeks it was on exhibition it only lost 2.8 seconds. In 1852 the clock was installed at the newly built King's Cross Railway Station in a tower which was 112 ft (34 m) in height. The 3 dials were 9 ft (2.7 m) in diameter. The clock survived until 1965 when it was replaced by Dent with an electric clock, yet another piece of history lost. However, the clock was not removed in its entirety as the bed and the pendulum are still in position.

Dent obtained the Council medal for this clock for 'its strength and accuracy' together with his use of a less expensive mode of construction than used in other comparable clocks.

Other firms particularly noted for turret clocks were Thwaites & Reed, Smiths of Derby, John Moore & Sons of Clerkenwell, J.W. Benson, J. Smith & Sons of Clerkenwell, Whitehurst & Son of Derby, J.B. Joyce of Whitchurch, G. & F. Cope of Nottingham and Gillett & Johnston, this last firm and John Smith & Sons of Derby are still in existence today. Whitehurst was founded just before the start of the Victorian era and was eventually acquired in 1855 by Roskell but not long after this the firm was wound up.

J. Tripplin in his account of the Paris Exhibition of 1889 on pp. 71–4 says a lot about Gillett & Johnson. Apparently they were able to secure an area of only 3 ft (0.9 m) square but made good use of this by displaying models. They showed a model of an automatic ringing machine and another 5 ft (152 cm) in height of Willing's Jubilee Clock Tower in Brighton. This showed the time on four dials and also operated a time ball. Surprisingly enough they also had a clock on the Eiffel Tower which apparently greatly surprised some of their French competitors! It had a dial 6 ft (183 cm) in diameter, struck the hours on a bell of 2½ cwt (127 kg) and the quarters on two bells each half of this weight. President Carnot inaugurated the starting of the clock in the Eiffel Tower in July 1889, when he formally set the wheels in motion. Tripplin records that the firm was founded in 1844 and then employed 80 people; the area covered by the works being 1,624 sq yd (1,358 sq m), and that it should be noted that they cast their own bells.

Smith & Sons of Derby were commissioned in 1882 to make a new clock for St Paul's. This was done under the direction of E.J. Denison or, as he had then become, Lord Grimthorpe.

J. Smith & Sons of St John's Square, Clerkenwell, exhibited a turret clock in the second Great International Exhibition held in South Kensington in 1862. This was on a smaller scale being intended for a tower on a summer house. There were four dials each 3 ft 6 in (107 cm) in diameter. It was a striking clock that went for eight days on a winding and had maintaining power. They also exhibited a second turret clock which had rack striking so as to prevent the incorrect striking that can occur with those with a count wheel. It had Vulliamy's version of the dead-beat escapement, that is the pallets are set into turned grooves, so that the depth can be set exactly, and should the pallets be dressed can be reset to their original position. The frames were of iron and so constructed that any part could be removed without disturbing the remaining parts. The wheels were of gun metal and the pinions of steel. The maintaining power was bolt and shutter and there was a micrometric beat-setting arrangement. The pendulum was unusual in that it had a spherical bob with a rod of varnished pine.

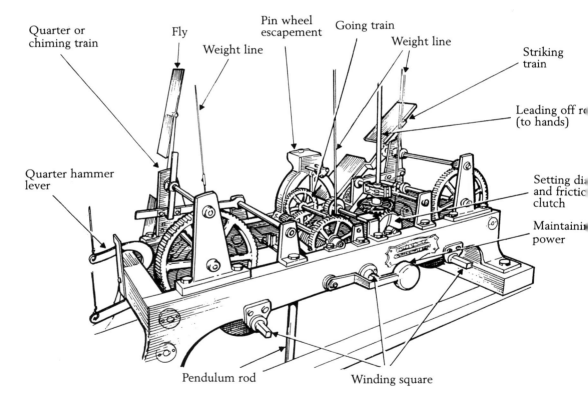

Figs (xvii) and (xviii) Flat-bed clocks
In the engineering sense there is no bed, flat or otherwise, connected with this type of clock frame. However, fig. (xvii) shows how the term originates for with this particular design all of the members that support the wheels and escapement are fixed to the same flat surface which is the edge of the main frame. There is no comparable layout used in any other type of clock. Some flat-bed turret clocks will be found in this section which look a lot more like a conventional plated frame clock with pillars and back and front plate. Nevertheless, if they are not the birdcage frame clock they are then called flat-bed and it is no use flying in the face of custom, even if the result is confusing.

Tripplin's account of the 1889 Paris Exhibition comments on the superiority of English turret clocks over those made in France. Whereas the French appeared to favour train or escapement remontoires the English in general favoured the gravity escapement. English pendulums tended to be of the zinc and iron type as opposed to the grid-iron favoured by the French. Also they were heavier, weighing from 100–500 lb (45–227 kg) with cylindrical bobs and from 6–14 ft (1.8–4.3 m) in length. The French pendulums usually beat seconds and were of an average weight of 40 lb (18 kg). They did, however, use the same type of frame namely the flat bed, and indeed it is probable that

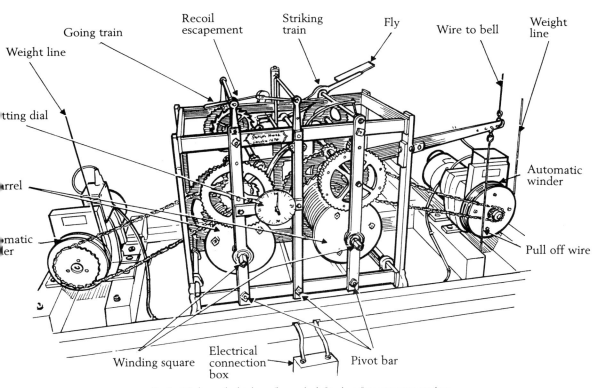

Fig. (xviii) shows the birdcage frame clock fixed up for automatic winding.
There is an excellent booklet on the various solutions to winding electrically, it is *An Amateur's Guide to Automatic Winders* by David Nettell, Macclesfield, 1987. It is an absolute mine of information on the topic and provides information impossible to obtain elsewhere.
The great advantage of the flat-bed clock is that nearly every part can be removed without having to disturb any other part. This enormously simplifies the problem of servicing these clocks. The illustrations come from a booklet published by the Council for the Care of Churches in 1982 called *Turret Clocks: Recommended Practice for Repair and Maintenance.*

they were the first to use this design. Although the great clock of Westminster was the first really important clock to use the flat bed construction in England it was not in fact the first to be made on these lines in this country.

It is very unfortunate that so many turret clocks have been consigned to the scrap heap during the period following the Second World War. As the cost of maintaining them and keeping them wound spiralled, so they were often discarded in favour of synchronous mains clocks. Special heavy-duty types of these synchronous clocks are made and there is not even a need for lead off work since they are cheap enough to fit one behind each dial and they will of course remain in synchronism. Naturally if this course is followed the bells will no longer be actuated and many a fine clock tower must now be condemned to silence. There is of course an alternative if it is only the difficulty of a winding that has to be overcome, for by the end of the nineteenth century electrical winding was becoming commonplace. Even the great clock of St Paul's made by John Smith & Sons of Derby in 1892 was eventually converted to electrical winding in 1965. The cast-iron flat-bed frame of this clock is 19 ft (5.8 m) in length, the hour hands are 5 ft 6 in (1.7 m) long, the minute hands 9 ft 6 in (2.9 m). The escapement is of course the double three-legged gravity since Lord Grimthorpe was consulted as to its design. He also had a new bell made, Great Paul; this was made by Taylor of Loughborough and weighs no less than 16 tons 14 cwt (16,968 kg), 3 tons 3 cwt (3,200 kg) more than Big Ben! However, this bell was never actually incorporated into the clock and is tolled only at one o'clock, in the middle of the day, and on special occasions.

Naturally not everyone is overjoyed at having a quarter-striking clock marking their sleepless hours and many mechanical clocks are provided with a silencing device that comes into operation during the night hours. This is a complication also found in domestic clocks and I must say to me a very welcome one. Although I don't mind the refined tinkle of a French clock, in general I find striking one of the more irksome of the complications that clocks have. I can understand why it was so common in times when illumination was a problem. Any of us who have had to struggle to live by candlelight during a power cut know how little can be seen. Nor must it be thought that candles were used in any great numbers even in households that could afford a clock since wax candles especially were always an expensive item. They were used sparingly and only the very rich used a lot and then only on special occasions. This seems to me to be the likely explanation of the popularity of striking work.

However, everything changed with the introduction of gas lighting and it is hard to see an explanation for the continued popularity of striking which we know to be a fact since it is even included in quartz clocks today. Is it just that old habits die hard? Surely however a more useful addition to a timepiece is calendar work, more applicable to a device that is intended to measure time and in fact requiring less parts in number and less complicated parts to boot. Not only that, but most of us get so used to the striking of a familiar clock that we cease to hear it except of course when we are listening to a quiet passage of music which is then successfully ruined!

Visibility: When a clock dial is a considerable distance from the ground its size has to bear a relationship to its height for it to be readable.

A record of some of the figures to hand will tell us what decisions have been made in the past. They are as follows:

Great George Dials	25 ft (7.6 m) diam.	Tower	220 ft (67 m).
Big Ben Dials	23 ft (7 m) diam.	Tower	180 ft (55 m).
St Paul's	17 ft (5.2 m) diam.	Tower	126 ft (38.4 m).
People's Palace, Mile End	5 ft (1.5 m) diam.	Tower	45 ft (13.7 m).
Mechlin	40 ft (12.2 m) diam.	Tower	300 ft (91.4 m).
St Pancras Station	13 ft (4 m) diam.	Tower	150 ft (45.7 m).
King's Cross Station	9 ft (2.7 m) diam.	Tower	90 ft (27.4 m).
Bow Church	9 ft (2.7 m) diam.	Tower	70 ft (21.3 m).
Manchester Infirmary	9 ft (2.7 m) diam.	Tower	80 ft (24.4 m).
Royal Exchange	9 ft (2.7 m) diam.	Tower	90 ft (27.4 m).
St George's Church, Leeds	8 ft (2.4 m) diam.	Tower	60 ft (18.3 m).
St Luke's, Chelsea	6 ft (1.8 m) diam.	Tower	72 ft (21.9 m).
Marylebone Church	3 ft (0.9 m) diam.	Tower	60 ft (18.3 m).
The Queen's Stables	6 ft (1.8 m) diam.	Tower	50 ft (15.2 m).

It will be seen from this that one can take as a rough rule that the diameter of the dial should be about one-ninth of its height above the ground.

In Vaudrey Mercer's book on Dent there is a section on turret clocks which details those sold before 1877 culled from a booklet published in May of that year. This was entitled 'Some of the tower clocks designed and manufactured, Bells Hung, etc., by E. Dent & Co., 61 Strand, 34 & 35 Royal Exchange, London (Factory – Gerrard Street)'. In the preface to this booklet is a statement which contradicts my findings as to the relationship between the size of a dial and its height above the ground since it states that it should be 1 ft (30.5 cm) in diameter for every 12 ft (3.7 m) in height above the ground. However, it will be seen that some individual examples above conform to this ratio.

The booklet then gave a list of 187 turret clocks divided into five different sizes, No. 5 being the largest and No. 1 the smallest. Fifteen are size 5, twenty are size 4, sixty are size 3, fifty-four are size 2, thirty-two are size 1, six are described as special and one is the Westminster Clock. Twenty-three of these clocks went abroad to places as far apart as Calcutta and Mexico.

Although details of the dial sizes and the bells are often given, technical details of the escapement, for instance, are seldom mentioned.

It is of interest that one of the clocks that was destined for somewhere in Doncaster did not have a dial at all! It was a size 5 clock striking the hours on a bell weighing a ton (1,016 kg) and the three-quarters upon four bells of proportionate weight.

It is obvious from the foregoing that this side of their business must have been very important to Dents.

Big Ben

The story of Big Ben, or the Westminster Clock as it should be called, is a long and complicated one (Big Ben is actually the hour bell but there is no use denying common usage and Big Ben will be the clock from now on). There will be no attempt to tell the story fully here, there are several comprehensive accounts of the clock already in existence and the reader is referred to the Bibliography for these. However, a few words must be said about this most famous clock.

The Clock at the Royal Exchange In truth it was the clock for the Royal Exchange that started the story. This clock was quoted for by three firms: Vulliamy, Whitehurst of Derby and E. Dent. There was some ill-feeling engendered because the job went to Dent. He had never made a turret

Opposite **Fig. (xix)**

clock but was determined to obtain the contract and quoted a price that was so low that he was assured of success. After only a year the clock was completed. Perhaps it was just as well that Dent came fresh to the scene since Airy had a great deal to do with the design of this clock and many new features were incorporated. One stipulation Airy made was that, as with Big Ben, the first stroke of the hour should be correct to the second, a thing that nearly all of the clockmakers of the period considered impossible.

Fig. (xix) shows the chiming clock in position. It has a curious layout with the larger work in one section and three separate sections mounted on top of this main part that take the escapement and its remontoire and the lighter components of the striking and chiming trains. Mounted in front of these latter two sections are the two count wheels and their levers. The train remontoire and the maintaining power were both to a new design of Airy's. The escapement was a dead beat. The pendulum was of the zinc and steel variety, it was a two-second, being 14 ft (4.2 m) long and weighing nearly 4 cwt (203 kg).

The view of the leading off work is unusually complete as one can also see one of the dials. Because of the position of the clock relative to the dials the leading off work is quite complicated with a multiplicity of gears to get from the clock to the hands. Because of this there could well have been a problem with backlash at the minute hands.

Big Ben   The Houses of Parliament, as we now know them, were rebuilt at a cost of £2,198,000 in the Victorian era and in 1844 the tower which was to house the clock was nearing completion and the business of ordering the clock was put in hand. Once again there was a good deal of unpleasantness. Vulliamy was first asked to submit plans for the clock but even before he had completed these E.J. Dent asked to be considered, not just to make to Vulliamy's drawings but also to do his own design. At this point the Commissioners realised that they had made a mistake in not making the whole affair competitive from the start and approached the Astronomer Royal, Airy, for advice. As Airy had already had very satisfactory dealings with Dent over the Royal Exchange clock he suggested that Dent should make the clock but that an element of competition should be introduced to ensure a reasonable price.

Airy drew up the conditions for the clock and these were onerous to a degree, so much so that again clockmakers said it was impossible to conform to them. At this time only three clockmakers were considered able to make the clock and, as before, they were Dent, Vulliamy and Whitehurst of Derby. They were each invited to tender. In the event Vulliamy's designs were not accepted and it was between Dent's tender of £1,500 and Whitehurst's (used to run-of-the-mill turret clocks) of £3,373. Of course there was no contest. Ultimately Dents were to be paid £1,800 after discussions between not only Airy and Dent but also a newcomer on the scene Denison – recommended by Airy, and the order was placed in 1852.

The clock was placed in position in 1859 after being finished and working in Dent's workshop for no less than four years!

E.J. Dent had died in 1853 and the clock was in fact finished by his stepson Frederick Dent although this was only after much legal argument as to whether he could inherit the contract. The clock was no sooner in position than it stopped, being unable to drive the heavy minute hands. These hands were designed by the architect Sir Charles Barry who decided to ignore Dent's advice and the result was hands that weighed no less than 6½ cwt (330 kg). Dent redesigned them and they then weighed 2 cwt (101.6 kg) and no more trouble was experienced from this source.

The bells, made by the firm of Mears, were to prove a much bigger problem than the clock and satisfactory striking did not occur until 1863 and then only after Airy had been asked for his recommendations. The biggest bell 'Big Ben', had cracked; Airy advised that it was turned so as to present a sound surface for the hammer to strike and also that the weight of the hammer should be halved. The result of following these recommendations is that we still hear the same bell to this very day.

The contract to look after Big Ben is held by Elliot's of Croydon, who purchased the firm of clock makers Thwaites & Reed and with it the Big Ben contract.

We owe this magnificent clock to four people; Airy, Denison, and the two Dents and I think it would be difficult to say just exactly how much was contributed by each of them. Details now follow on both Airy and Denison.

George Biddel Airy was Astronomer Royal from 1835 to 1881 and was knighted in 1874, he died in 1892 aged 90.

He had a great interest in horology as evidenced by his part in the story of the Royal Exchange clock and Big Ben. He was scientific adviser to the Admiralty upon chronometers and was greatly interested in them. He was a considerate and painstaking critic of any plans submitted to him by chronometer makers and usually wrote at length to advise them.

Edmund Denison, Junior, was born in 1816 and was educated at Doncaster, Eton and Trinity College, Cambridge. Called to the bar in 1841 he was a commanding figure, capable, self-confident and of a strong personality. He was made a Queen's Council in 1854 and was soon to become acknowledged leader of the Parliamentary bar.

It is thought that his interest in horology came from his association with James McKensie Bloxham, a fellow barrister who was himself to invent a form of gravity escapement. Denison's interest was so awakened that he studied the subject seriously and published a book *Rudimentary Treatise on Clocks* in 1850. This is how he came to be asked in 1851 by Lord Seymour, then First Commissioner of Works, to act with Airy regarding the new clock for the Palace of Westminster and this clock was to contain the gravity escapement designed by Denison.

After Frederick Dent's death in 1860 there was unpleasantness over his will and Denison was no longer welcome at Dent's premises. Accordingly he chose another clockmaker William Potts to help him in his experiments. The fact that Potts worked in Leeds apparently caused no difficulty.

Denison was asked after the completion of the Westminster Clock to give a lecture to the British Horological Institute and this was to lead to him being elected to the office of President of the Institute in 1868, which position he held until he died in 1905.

139 *The Westminster Clock*

This clock was the largest made in the Victorian era. The clocktower is 40 ft (12.2 m) square and the dials 180 ft (55 m) above ground level, and are each 22½ ft (6.9 m) in diameter. The minute hands are 11 ft (3.4 m) long with counterpoises 3 ft (0.9 m) long. For lightness these hands are of copper and hollow, with strengthening ribs at intervals.

The movement has a frame 15½ ft (4.7 m) long and 4 ft (1.2 m) in depth. There are three weight-driven trains. The going train is in the centre and it has a three-legged gravity escapement. The 2-second pendulum weighs 685 lb (311 kg), it is of the zinc and iron type. Because it is so heavy the pendulum does not hang from the movement but from a heavy cast-iron bracket fixed directly to the outside wall.

To the left of the going train is the striking train which is released by the going train *not* by the chiming train. This is because the design had to be such that the striking commenced within a second of the correct time. To this end the chime at the hour is let off 20 seconds early, and there is a system of double warning. The second cam that holds the striking and lets it off so accurately can do so since it rotates rapidly, once in 15 minutes in fact.

To avoid any uncertainty that might occur in the time taken for the hour hammer to drop, it is raised and then allowed to fall once released by the 15-minute cam.

Chiming is of course done by the train on the right.

The going train is as follows:

Great wheel 180 driving a pinion of 48 for the hand work, and one of 12 on which the second wheel of 120 is mounted. The second wheel drives a pinion of 16 which carries the third wheel of 90 this in turn driving the escape pinon of 9. The escape wheel is 12 in (30.5 cm) in diameter.

The bells are as follows:

The hour bell (Big Ben), 13 tons 11 cwt (13,769 kg), struck by a hammer weighing 4 cwt (203 kg).

The four quarter bells weigh 78, 33, 26 and 21 cwt (3,963, 1,702, 1,321 and 1,067 kg) respectively.

The drawing of the clock (fig. 139a) is provided with a key to give extra information.

For further details see Vaudrey Mercer's book, *Edward John Dent and his Successors*, London, 1977 and *The Book of Big Ben* by Alfred Gilgrass London, 1946.

The four pairs of hands are driven by four horizontal lead-off rods, each with its own set of motion work. The connection between the movement and the minute arbors is through the bevel wheels B, B, B, and B and the oblique shaft D.

Chiming the Quarters

The quarter striking is controlled by the snail Q which turns once an hour. The quarter train is held by the locking lever F which rests on the upper of two blocks on the lever H. Lever K engages with lever H and as the quarter approaches the snail presses down lever K until it allows lever F to escape from the upper locking block to the lower block thus allowing warning to occur. The quarter is sounded when the lever H falls free of the locking lever F and the quarter train begins to run. Lever H is lifted sufficiently

by the double cam G during warning to disengage the tongue P from the notch of the locking plate N in which its rests.

The locking plate N makes one revolution in 3 hours.

The speed of chiming is regulated by the vertical standing fly A.

Fig. 139a Key to the Westminster Clock drawing

A	Fly.
B	Bevel Wheel Drives To Hands.
C	Bevel Wheel Drive from Clock.
D	Shaft Between B and C.
E	Fly Controlling Speed of Striking.
F	Locking Lever.
G	Cam.
H	Lever.
J	Cam-like Teeth For Lifting Hammers.
K	Lever.
L	Locking Plate.
M	Lever.
N	Great Wheel.
P	Tongue.
Q	Quarter Snail.

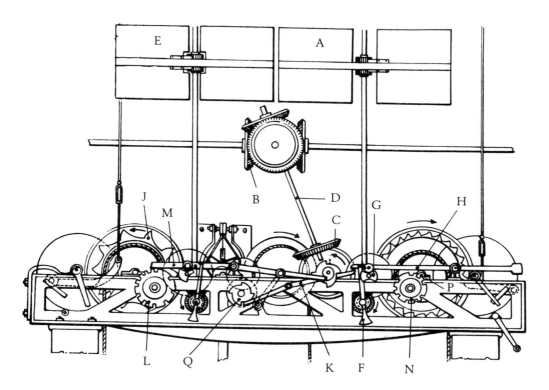

Striking the Hour

The striking is let off in much the same way as the chiming except that there is double warning. This is necessary because of the stringent requirement that the first blow struck at each hour should be accurate to a second as given by the clock. Therefore, after the first warning the train is held by a second locking lever which is released by a cam on the 15-minute wheel of the escapement. This cam moves with the pendulum in 2-second jumps and allows the second locking lever to drop off at the 58th second i.e., the last

beat but one before the hour. At the completion of the previous strike the hour hammer was left in the lifted position or at least almost completely lifted. On being released at the 58th second the train just has sufficient time to get going, to complete the raising of the hammer and to allow it to fall exactly on time.

Little is usually said about the logistic problems connected with raising a bell weighing over 13 tons (13,210 kg) a height of 190 ft (58 m), but there is an account in *The Illustrated London News* for 16 October 1868. I think the most interesting

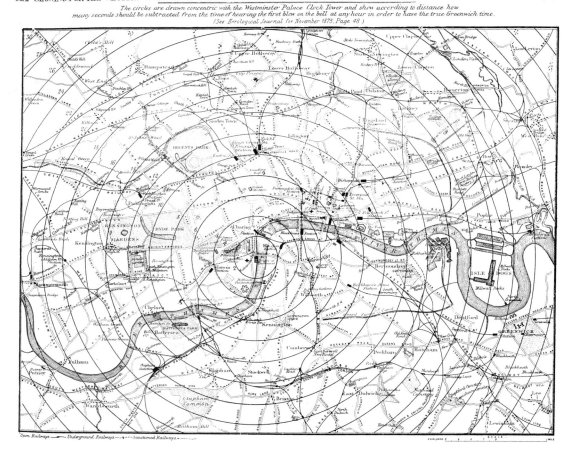

MAP SHOWING FOR THE WESTMINSTER CLOCK BELL THE ALLOWANCE OF TIME TO BE MADE ON ACCOUNT OF THE VELOCITY OF SOUND

The circles are drawn concentric with the Westminster Palace Clock Tower and show according to distance how many seconds should be subtracted from the time of hearing the first blow on the bell at any hour in order to have the true Greenwich time.

(See Horological Journal for November 1875, Page 48.)

Fig. 139b A map was produced to help people to tell what allowance they should make if they were hearing Big Ben over a distance. Concentric rings were drawn around the position of the clock on a map at intervals of a seconds travel for the sound. Obviously the direction and strength of the wind could not be allowed for but nevertheless it was better than making

no allowance at all. If you lived at Cricklewood then the map told you that the sound took 26 seconds to reach you, so that this had to be allowed for if you wanted to know the true time. Just how far the sound would travel on a quiet night I do not know, I suspect not as far as Cricklewood!

fact is that a special chain had to be made nearly 1,800 ft (549 m) long. When it is realised that this is about a third of a mile (536 m) in length one cannot help but be impressed. The reason for needing such a length is that the bell was raised using a multiple pulley system. Because of the mechanical advantage of the system only eight men turning two handles were needed to perform the task.

The first of the large bells that was cast was found to be cracked and this was broken up preparatory to recasting. There were very few firms in the world capable of making such bells and that remains true today.

140 *Chiming Turret Clock*
by J.W. Benson, 1889

Made for the Portsmouth Town Hall as witness the plaque attached to the clock which says: *A.D. 1889 THIS CLOCK WAS MADE TO THE ORDER OF THE MAYOR AND COR-*

PORATION OF PORTSMOUTH BY J.W. BENSON CLOCKMAKER TO HER MAJESTY THE QUEEN. 42 & 44 LUDGATE HILL, LONDON.

Unusually we have a drawing of the clock in position in its tower so that we can see the full detail of how everything is arranged (fig. 140a). The lead-off work to the hands goes directly up from the clock with the bevel gears necessary for the changes in direction.

In the central part of the rod are the two yokes which act as a universal joint and take up any out of alignment. To set the scale the dials are 11 ft (3.4 m) in diameter.

The whole clock without the weights, pendulum, hammers or dials weighs about 2½ tons (2,540 kg)! The hands are of hammered copper counterpoised and whose arbors run on friction rollers. The horizontal bed is 9 ft (2.7 m) in length and of solid cast iron. The wheels are gun metal and the steel pinions cut from the solid, hardened, tempered and polished.

All the pivots are in gun-metal bearings screwed into the frame so that any part may be taken out separately.

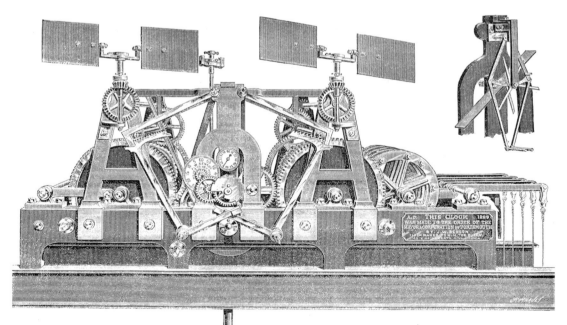

Fig. 140a

The 2-second pendulum has zinc and iron temperature compensation and it and the cast-iron bob weigh over 3 cwt (152 kg). The total length of the pendulum is 15 ft (4.6 m). The escapement is the double three-legged gravity as in the Westminster Clock.

---

141 *The 'Trophy' Turret Clock*
by J.W. Benson displayed in the 1862 International Exhibition

This large clock was meant to be an eye-catcher and it certainly must have been since it was situated in the central avenue of the exhibition building. The illustrations show a general view of the clock (fig. 141a), and a front elevation. The movement, has a dead-beat escapement, accuracy being achieved by means of a remontoire in the train. The escape wheel rotates once every two minutes as is evident from the seconds dial which is marked 1–60 twice. Since the escape wheel has 30 teeth this means that the clock had a 2-second pendulum since the seconds hand is on the extended pivot of the escape pinion.

Around the top of the base of the clock casing there were exhibited a 'curious collection of antique watches, with a view to illustrating the gradual rise and progress of watchmaking to the present time'. This is an early indication of an interest in antique watches and doubly surprising in that it was by a purely commercial firm. The size of the clock can be judged from the figures standing by it.

Benson received an Honourable Mention in the 1862 Exhibition.

This clock, exhibited by Benson, was actually made by Gillett & Bland.

James William Benson were in business from 1849–1973. They were at Cornhill from 1849–64, at Ludgate Hill from 1854–1937, at 25, Old Bond Street from 1872–3, and had a factory at 38, Bell Sauvage Yard from 1892–1937. They traded as Samuel Suckley & J.W. Benson from 1854–5, and J.W. Benson from 1856–91. From 1892–1973 they became a limited liability company.

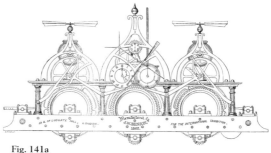

Fig. 141a

142 *Display Chiming Turret Clock*

Anonymous, *c.* 1900

The substantial oak cabinet is flanked by barley-twist columns with a glazed upper section to display the mechanism. The cresting bears the motto *Toujours Jamais!* (always never).

The mechanism is a small turret chiming clock with lead-off work to the dial above. The silvered dial is 14 in (35.6 cm) in diameter and has gilt Roman numerals. The hands are Gothic style and of blued steel.

The going side of the clock has a dead-beat escapement which is driven by a 30-second

remontoire. It is provided with maintaining power.

Either one of two chimes can be selected and there are nine tubular gongs which can be seen on the right-hand side of the upper part of the case. The massive chiming weight is also on this side of the case. A multi-pulley arrangement increases the effective drop.

H. 8 ft 2 in (249 cm), W. 4 ft 7 in (140 cm).

This clock was on display in the Children's Gallery at the Science Museum from 1964 to 1980 when the then owner decided it should be sold.

142

143 *Chiming Turret Clock Movement*

by Gillett and Johnston of Croydon, *c.* 1890

This fine drawing of a top of the range turret clock movement by Gillett and Johnston shows every detail of the mechanism.

The cast iron frame is designed to take up as little space as possible. Obviously the clock is intended to be set high in a tower, so it must be kept small; this is shown by the fact that the striking cables run down from the movement, not up. With this movement the hours could be struck on a bell weighing as much as 6 tons. The time could be shown on dials up to 9 ft in diameter. The driving weights would have been nearly a ton. The wheels would have been of gun metal and the pinions of cast steel.

There is a double three-legged gravity escapement as fitted to Big Ben, so that the performance of the clock would not be affected by high winds or snow upon the hands.

The small weight on the left hand side below the movement is for the maintaining power, this is lifted during winding of the going train. Note the ratchet on each of the fly arbors which prevent the striking or chiming train from suffering the strain of having to suddenly halt the fly whilst it is rotating at full speed. Because it can ratchet, the fly can carry on rotating for a time even though its arbor has come to a halt.

Note the tell-tale dial which enables the clock

to be set to time without one being able to see the hands. This has five minute and minute marks. The arbor on which the setting handle is mounted also carries a cam with four lobes, clearly seen in the drawing; this is the quarter cam which actuates the chiming.

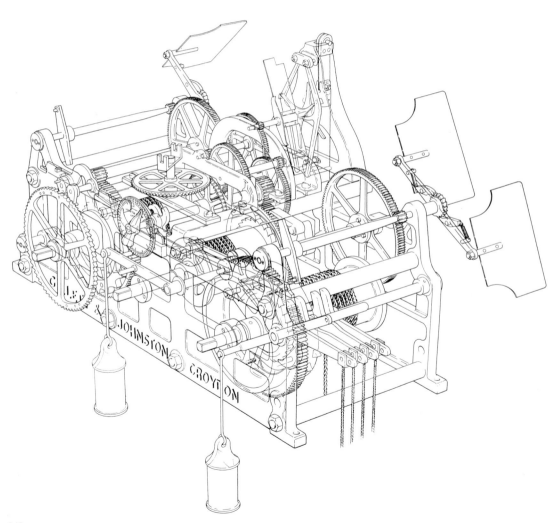

Appendices

I The Great Exhibitions

The Victorian era was a marvellous time for great international exhibitions and the world of horology was not slow to show off its wares. It was not just the big firms that got the plaudits either, for in the later exhibitions the individual craftsman also obtained recognition.

The following is a list of the major exhibitions:

1851 The 'Great Exhibition' Held in Hyde Park
1855 The Paris Exhibition
1862 London the 'Second Great International Exhibition'
1865 London (not International)
1867 Paris
1871 London
1872 London
1873 Vienna
1875 Paris
1876 London (not International) South Kensington, Loan Collection of Scientific Instruments
1876 Philadelphia
1878 Paris
1878 Melbourne
1885 International Inventions Exhibition
1889 Paris
1893 Chicago
1900 Paris

It is of interest that once the 1851 Exhibition had made these international displays fashionable, London held no less than six in the first twenty-five years, whereas other countries only held three. In the next twenty-five years, however, London held not one. This is very strange and perhaps indicates either complacency among the English or that the rot was already setting in and industry was having a hard time.

1851   The Great Exhibition

This great exhibition was held at Hyde Park in the specially built Crystal Palace and gives us a chance to see what were considered to be the outstanding pieces of the period.

Great efforts were made by those wishing to exhibit to produce new ideas and the result was a rash of patent applications which in 1852 led to a reorganisation and simplification of the patent system. This, in turn, led to an increase in the number of patents being applied for and anyone who wants some enjoyable reading could do worse than dip into the digest of patents, reprints of which have recently been published. Some of the things patented were so ridiculous that you can but wonder at the people responsible. However, there are of course those which are of great interest and these tell us not only the name of the patentee but also when the patent was taken out.

In this exhibition E.J. Dent won a Council Medal for his turret clock and a collection of other articles.

Prize medals were won by the following:
Charles Frodsham: Chronometers and watches
J. Gowland: Astronomical clock
J. Hutton: Chronometers
E.T. Loseby: Chronometer balance
Charles MacDowall: Clock escapement
Parkinson & Frodsham: Chronometers and watches
R. Roberts: Turret clock

1855   The Paris Exhibition

At this exhibition Thomas Cole was told by the judges that he held 'a very distinguished position for true artistic excellence and workmanship'. For more on Cole's work and the work of his imitators see Chapter 3.

Charles Frodsham also won a gold medal of honour, see the section 'Wall and Table Regulators' p. 127 for a record of this achievement engraved on one of his clock dials.

1862   The Second Great Exhibition

Much of the subsequent information on exhibitions has been gleaned from the pages of the *Horological Journal* (*H.J.*). Anything in quotation marks is directly quoted. For other sources see the Bibliography.

This second Great Exhibition was held at South Kensington and was unfortunately not as successful as the first. In fact there was an overall loss of £10,000 when the exhibition closed. There was no lack of exhibitors, 315 all told, of whom 114 were British. Not surprisingly the other two countries represented in force were Switzerland (74 exhibitors) and France (54 exhibitors). Thus Great Britain nearly outnumbered the other two combined. Although it was agreed that the English display was good it was also claimed that it could have been far better. As was said in the *H.J* for December 1862 p. 40 'From the names of the exhibitors we certainly missed many who enjoy a wide and familiar reputation, possibly superior to any necessity for any further publicity.' This was deplored and of course rightly so.

There was a fine display of temperature compensation balances, among those mentioned were examples by Hartnup, Loseby, Kullberg and Cole: the latter two gained medals. The chronometers were reported as representing much excellence of workmanship with special mention of the high finish of Kullberg's display. It was claimed that 'the Clock division was greatly deficient in variety and display of invention; electricity and gravity escapements yielding the only ground for operation. Mr Cooke of York distinguished himself for judicious form and adoption, both in the great work and escapement, for turret machinery'. Cooke won a medal for his work. 'Mr Hislop exhibited a successful adaptation of the train of wheels to show sidereal time, driven by the main time train, in one clock, which is a useful combination for observatories.' In fact William Hislop received an honourable mention for this clock. Also mentioned was that: 'Some highly artistically designed clock cases were displayed by T. Cole, White and Howell & James.' Cole and White were given medals. Doubtless the cases displayed by Howell & James were also made by Cole.

Joseph Sewill was reported as being the only exhibitor from Liverpool. Although the major part of what he showed was watches he also showed marine chronometers; he gained a medal.

E.D. Johnson F.R.A.S., of 9 Wilmington Square was a juror but although thus not eligible for any awards exhibited many items among which there was a 'magnetic dispencer which caused a marine chronometer to revolve on its own axis every 24 hours'. The object of this was 'to subject the instrument in all positions to the inductive influence of the magnetism of the ship, and preventing the balance and steel work from acquiring magnetic polarity'. Johnson also showed many items to do with pendulums.

S. Holdsworth of Islington showed every type of horological component connected with horology, made from jewels of many kinds. Among the items mentioned were diamond and sapphire files for shortening stone pallets and reducing hard steel. He had an honourable mention.

Not mentioned in the *H.J.*, a most strange omission, was the Great Clock by J.W. Benson found fully described in the previous chapter. Benson had an honourable mention.

Also omitted was the astronomical clock by T. Sherratt. This is to be found in the chapter on Mantel and Table Clocks.

Another omission, not so surprising, however, is comment on the display mounted by John Bennett, omitted no doubt because there was antipathy towards Bennett as far as the establishment was concerned. This omission is the worse since Bennett won a medal. However, there was a write-up in *Cassells Illustrated* in December 1862 which showed Bennett's stand and the time ball that crowned the display. As well as the illustration of Bennett's display I thought the write-up should be included as being of equal interest. Note that Bennett was the President of the Horological Section and yet still not mentioned in the *H.J.* Just before the end of the write-up the views of Bennett himself peep through when there is talk about the use of female labour 'this to ensure a mode of manufacture which shall cheapen the cost'. This was one of the very concepts that enraged the establishment. The other was the importation of goods from abroad, although it would seem that Bennett was not showing foreign goods at this exhibition.

In this same journal there were also illustrations of the Great Clock by J.W. Benson, mentioned above, together with another write-up which I quote in full.

When it is remembered that, in addition to the whole of the watches and clocks annually produced in England, we are under the necessity of importing for home consumption watches from Switzerland, and clocks from France and America, of more than £1,000,000 worth per annum, the importance of the Horological Department of the Great Exhibition will be manifest.

For this reason, and from the fact that, as the foreign manufacturers increased in amount of late years, the quantity manufactured at home has fallen off more than one-third since the year 1855, this year's display of the respective rivals was regarded with much interest on all sides; it is, therefore, satisfactory to know that, both in quantity and quality, the English manufacturer maintained a most creditable position. Indeed, several of the most eminent houses have produced chronometers, duplex and lever watches of the highest quality for scientific construction and for precision of performance: while as to the external form and decoration, it was clear that the application of art to this branch of manufacture has made considerable advance in the last ten years.

In clocks of a scientific construction the English have always been pre-eminent. As far back as 1715, the astronomical regulator was brought to absolute perfection by George Graham, whose escapement and pendulum are those

Fig. (xx)

perfection of horological science, that Mr. Bennett produced
and exhibited a chronometer, a regulator, and the time ball,
the results of which in action were absolutely coincident for
days and weeks together. This is the more striking, since
these three very remarkable instruments were totally distinct
in their organisation, their arrangements, and their motive
and controlling powers – the chronometer moved with its
mainspring and its balance; the regulator by its mercurial
pendulum, and its weight, and the law of gravitation; while
the huge time-ball descended with undeviating regularity,
detached at every hour by the electric current from the
Royal Observatory at Greenwich. Thus, so far as perfect
precision can go, nothing more exact can be required. The
lesson taught by this international display proved to the
English workman that his best energies must be steadily
directed to external elegance, to the higher cultivation of the
fine arts as applicable to his mechanical production, and,
above all, by a better system, and perhaps, by enlisting the
valuable assistance of the female hand, to insure a mode of
manufacture which shall cheapen the cost of production.
The English must produce a watch good enough and cheap
enough for the million; they must give the maximum of
quality at the minimum of cost, and then it will be admitted
that this great concourse of manufacturing ingenuity has not
been organised in vain, and that the beneficial effect in this,
as well as in many other departments, will have tended alike
to the advantage of the consumer and the producer. The
manufacturer will flourish, the workman will enjoy the
remuneration he so richly deserves, and will find the means
of attaining a higher and more honourable social position;
while among the whole world of watch-buyers the next
generation may hope to see, in days of more strict
punctuality and more swift locomotion, that it will become
for every man and every woman as much the custom to
wear an elegant watch as to possess an enlightened head.

Others who received awards are as follows:

Medals: Adams & Son, Barraud & Lund, G. Blackie,
W.B. Crisp, H. Delholme, M.F. Dent, Ganeval &
Canard, Guiblet & Rambal, S. and J. Hewitt, J.
McLennon, W. Molyneux, B. & J. Moore, P. Pendleton,
E. Saggerson, Smith & Sons, J. Walker, A. P. Walsh and
J. Wycherley.

Honourable mentions were also given to:

J. Brock, Camerer, Kuss & Co., Dr Clarke, Davis &
Sons, T. Deitman, J. Fairer, Frodsham & Baker, C.G.
Gumpel, J. Hawkbury, C.J. Hill, Howell James & Co.,
Hunt & Roskell, J. Jones, C. Lange, B. Marriott, T.
Mercer, W. Morris, Muirhead & Son, J. Murray, J. Neal,
G.J. Oram, S.A. Petit, Plaskett & Son, Porthouse &
French, T. Quaife, T. Russell & Son, Samuel & Son, J.
Saunders, W.G. Schoof, C. Shepherd, Thompson &
Profaze.

*1865   Exhibition of the Arts and Manufactures of
North-East London held at Islington*
Although not international there was a good
horological display in this exhibition.

E.D. Johnson was to the forefront again, among
other things he showed a model clock tower 4 ft

still used for the most precise astronomical purposes at the
present day; and it is equally true that in clocks chiming the
quarters, suitable for the baronial hall, no foreign
manufacturer has ventured to compete with this specialty of
English workmanship. Fine specimens in the three points, for
the use of the navigator, the astronomer, and the nobleman,
were displayed by such houses as Hislop, Delolme, Blackie,
Frodsham, and Bennett – the highest class of instruments, in
virtue of their extreme simplicity, in which respect the
English regulator and chronometer have long left no room
for improvement; while in the more complex and intricate
combination of mechanical contrivance, the Swiss produce
specimens which to the English workman is felt to be
forbidden ground; so also, whenever the clock is made an
article of ornament for the mantelpiece, the machine is held
to be of more importance as an object of art and beauty in
design, than as a scientific instrument. The Frenchman is
known to excel wherever the mind and delicate touch of the
artist is required to produce a thing of beauty and elegance,
and there France fairly merited the place of honour. In the
midst of so much variety and extent of horological products,
it would only create confusion to give a particular catalogue,
specifying every peculiarity of its form and construction. We
may take one example, the most prominent in the English
department, that of Mr. Bennett, Cheapside. As president of
his class, he felt bound to occupy such a position as would
have every principal branch of horology fully represented in
his case. It is a remarkable fact, demonstrating the absolute

(1.2 m) in height surmounted by a time ball designed as a centrepiece for a first-class horological shop window. Note that *his* display and time ball get a mention (see above). He also showed an engine for making parts of frames by copying.

R. Webster of 74 Cornhill, showed railway clocks, in other words English dial clocks. These were clocks with seconds pendulums which had wood rods with solid zinc cylindrical bobs 14 in (35.6 cm) long which Mr Webster said 'makes a good cheap compensation pendulum'. His dials were of glass, back painted to form a permanent white dial with black numerals. His cases were of teak, 'the greasiness of which wood keeps out the damp to which railway clocks are exposed'.

Victor Kullberg of 12 Cloudsley Terrace showed chronometers, one of which was beating at twice the normal rate. The purpose of this was to get the settling down period over in six months instead of its taking the normal year.

Thwaites Brothers of 163 St John Street Road showed a variety of clock dials.

J. Evans of 89 Mount Street, Berkley Square, exhibited a Congreve clock, an example of which is to be found in the chapter on skeleton clocks. The final comment by Mr Evans goes as follows: '. . . but at the best I can only look on them (Congreve clocks) as horological toys'. In this he was correct for the timekeeping of these clocks is abysmal.

S. Holdsworth of 54 Spencer Street, showed his jewels once again.

Other firms mentioned were:
J. Bennett, T. Leonard, B. Chevalier, Camerer & Co., J. Hammersley, Marriot & Langford, Smith & Sons, H.B. Crisp, J. Wright & Son and French & Co.

1867   The Paris Exhibition
There is an account of the horological instruments in the December issue of the *H.J.* In 1862 there were 300 exhibitors and in the 1867 a staggering 535. Not only were there more exhibitors but in general they showed more items each than were shown at the 1862 exhibition. English chronometer makers were singled out for praise, as was always the case in these exhibitions. A lot was written about middle temperature error (M.T.E.) and the devices for overcoming it.

Charles Frodsham was particularly mentioned as having developed the Micrometric Balance which could be adjusted without the need to take the balance from the chronometer or interfering with its mean time. Frodsham was a juror and because of that was precluded from competition for prizes. He also showed an astronomical regulator with a new brass tubular mercury compensation and connecting galvanic

apparatus for recording the time of observations. This clock was made for the Cambridge Observatory in the United States. It was reported to be a model of clock 991 made by him for the Melbourne Observatory. The results of the performance of this latter clock over a period of three years were submitted to the jury who pronounced it to be the most remarkable for accuracy on record. Charles Frodsham also showed a new type of mercurial pendulum where the mercury is in hermetically sealed glass tubes but held within a brass tube.

R. Parkinson & Frodsham, J. Poole, M.F. Dent, and of course Victor Kullberg all exhibited marine chronometers as well. There were not many turret clocks, J.W. Benson being the only English maker to exhibit one.

R. Claxon and S. Holdsworth showed clock, chronometer and watch jewels, set and unset. They consisted of diamonds, rubies, sapphires, chrysolites, garnets and aquamarines. As well as jewel holes for all purposes there were solid jewel impulse rollers, ruby cylinders, duplex rollers and all sorts of ruby pins.

After the event there was a bitter complaint from M.F. Dent who felt that they were being insulted by the award of a mere silver medal when in their opinion they should have had a gold. I am afraid that they put it down to the fact that Charles Frodsham was a juror, a man they looked upon as their chief rival. It was of course an argument that was incapable of being resolved. In the letters it became clear that there were only 18 or 19 English exhibitors to whom were granted 3 gold medals, 6 silver, 6 bronze and 3 honourable mentions. Frodsham said that had the overall number of medals not been severely restricted then Walker and Son, White and Sewill would all have had silver medals not bronze. He further said that the quality of the English marine chronometers was the admiration of all comers.

We learn from the account of the Paris exhibition of 1900 that Victor Kullberg won a gold medal at this 1867 exhibition.

1871   The International Exhibition
I could find no reference to this exhibition in the pages of the *H.J.*, there are however two clocks shown in the Exhibition Catalogue, these bearing the name Howell & James.

1875   'International Exhibition of Maritime and River Industries' in Paris
Only four English firms exhibited, Victor Kullberg, Reid & Sons, James Poole & Co. and Michael Riego. All exhibited chronometers and watches and all except Kullberg, who was disqualified because he was a juror, won awards.

1876   *The Scientific Loan Exhibition*
(This once again was not an international exhibition.)

The Editor of the *H.J.* was very critical of this exhibition for he felt that much more should have been done on the historical side of the horological world and called what was there a 'scanty display arranged apparently without any discrimination'. He added that viewed as a national effort it was positively humiliating!

There was a considerable display of compensation balances, 32 of them contributed by the Horological Institute.

Sir G.B. Airy's barometric compensation fitted to a regulator by E. Dent was on show.

Electric clocks on F.J. Ritchies plan were there and from the Postmaster General a regulator and apparatus for the distribution of Greenwich time current at provincial stations.

There was a clock with Mr Highams gravity escapement, and a detached gravity escapement by Mr Henry J. Lee.

Some historical objects were shown, among them Kendall's K.2., the chronometer destined for undying fame as that carried by Captain Bligh on his fateful voyage. Also on display was the Dover Castle clock, removed from there in 1872.

1878   *The Paris Exhibition*
Once again the editor was not happy and referred to 'the engineer of the British Commission having done his best with the meagre materials available but looking at the half dozen or so exhibits (there were incidentally eleven, tut tut Mr Editor!) no matter how judiciously they are arranged, it seems barely possible to believe that there is a Clerkenwell in London, or a Prescot in Lancashire, to say nothing of Coventry, of Liverpool, or even of Birmingham'. He also complained bitterly that Losada, although from London, exhibited in the Spanish section (he incidentally made up the 12th exhibitor from England, as curiously enough Riego exhibited in both the Spanish and the English sections).

Victor Kullberg to the fore as usual, had 21 marine chronometers there, one of especial interest since it beat 130 times per minute and had two balances, one a compensation balance and the other a plain brass balance. The fast beat was for facilitating observations and the plain balance was so arranged that it could be used as a chronometrical thermometer. He also showed a model of a dead-beat escapement that ran without oil, it having rollers instead of fixed stones. Kullberg, as was usually the case, won a gold medal.

R. Webster also showed a marine chronometer and received an honourable mention.

Riego had what was described as a beautiful turret clock movement with bronze wheels and solid pinions, it had a Graham dead-beat escapement. Riego received a bronze medal.

G.E. Frodsham also showed marine chronometers, they won a silver medal.

G.F. Price were not granted any honours and showed a turret clock with a double three-legged gravity escapement, a smaller 8-day striking turret clock with a Graham dead-beat escapement and a wood/rod pendulum. Yet a third turret clock had a double three-legged gravity escapement, and a one-and-a-half seconds pendulum with a 3 cwt (152 kg) bob.

Frederick Schick exhibited chains of all varieties for clocks, chronometers, watches and aneroid barometers, he gained a bronze medal.

Two exhibitors came in for scathing comments in the *H.J.*: Sir John Bennett, still at odds with the trade for selling so much that came from abroad and poor old Jenner & Knewstub, called the extensive advertisers of the 'Bag of Bags' whatever this meant and castigated for being 'mere tradesmen not people who invented or improved things'. The final sentence went thus 'It is a pity that the latter cannot be penetrated with a sufficient sense of the fitness of things to confine himself to the shop and the bazaar.' Take that!

Another firm to get an award was J. Houghton who got a bronze medal but what what they showed I do not know.

1885   *The International Inventions Exhibition*
This exhibition was held in South Kensington and we actually have a floor plan for the area where the exhibition took place. This plan shows how to reach the Horological area.

The following firms and organisations had Diplomas of Honour:

The British Horological Institute for a collective exhibit showing progress in technical training and illustrating high class manufacture.

The Kew Committee of the Royal Society for their system of testing watches.

Gold medals went to: E. Dent for the improvements to turret clocks and chronometers; Victor Kullberg (inevitably) for improvements and general excellence in the manufacture of marine chronometers.

Silver medals went to: A.H. Rowley for improvements in details of manufactures of clocks and watches; F. Sage for a watchman's clock; M. Stamper & Co., for an 8-day alarm; The Standard Time and Telephone Co. Ltd. for a method of synchronising clocks; R.G. Webster for a method of showing 24-hour time and other improvements in timekeeping.

Bronze medals went to: Camerer Kuss & Co. for modification in watchman's and other clocks; J. Harrington for the application of metal tubes as sounding pieces in chiming clocks; C. Shepherd for improvements in electrical and other sympathetic clocks; George Moore for clocks with electric alarm attachments.

Others who showed and were mentioned in the *H.J.* were: W. Barnsdale who showed a regulator of the finest quality and finish, a three-part quarter clock chiming on eight bells and gongs at the hours, a carriage timepiece and a second one that struck and repeated; H. Cousens showed clocks and timepieces with his patent dial whereby the numerals show as 1–12 during the first half of the day and 13–24 for the second half; J. Hammersly showed various marine chronometers as did H.P. Isaac, one of his chronometers is mentioned as having a balance with a palladium spring; Thomas Mercer came in for a lot of praise for his chronometers with special mention of his balance as described in David Glasgow's *Watch and Clockmaking*, p. 256.

Mercer also showed a chronometer with a 12 in (30.5 cm) dial for use as a portable regulator and a gilt chronometer clock that struck the hours and another similar that was a timepiece. W. Schoof was described as being responsible for a bold departure in his chronometer escapement which is to be found described in this volume in the chronometer chapter. R.G. Webster described as 'this old city house of repute' displayed Quarter clocks in unusually fine cases, a chronometer with a new type of compensation balance, a clock with both universal and local time and a regulator with an improved gravity escapement.

Victor Kullberg had the usual brilliant show of marine chronometers. One had a feature whereby the escape wheel was locked once the balance was removed.

N.C. Firth showed what was in effect a clocking-in clock with an ingenious and apparently foolproof way of preventing fraud. With this clock it was possible to see the exact order in which the employees arrived.

A.H. Rowley who as we know won a medal, showed a large chiming clock with calendar and automated figures. Their other exhibits also included ship's timepieces.

Frodsham and Co. also showed marine chronometers but although they won a medal this was for work connected with their watches.

E. Dent and Co., who (as already stated) won a gold medal, showed an astronomical clock with a mechanism for dropping a time ball. There was a new compensation pendulum (this was probably for the sidereal clock at Greenwich, and was the subject of a patent No. 9358 of the 5th August 1885). They also showed a galvanic chronograph, a chronometer with electrical contacts and a small turret clock with special improvements.

Gillett and Bland had on display a fine turret clock. They also showed a type of clock which they called a chronoscope. This had a digital display which the firm felt was particularly applicable to railway timekeepers and for giving 24 hour time. They would be pleased to know that this type of display is now the norm on our stations today. In the *H.J.* for May 1889, p. 139, there is a full report of their exhibits which reads as follows:

> Messrs. Gillett & Co., of Croydon, have just finished their exhibit for the Exhibition, which includes the following: — A ting tang quarter turret clock with Denison's double three-legged gravity escapement, solid pinions; the arbors have been nickel-plated, which, added to the finish of the other parts, makes it a fine specimen for exhibition. A model of an automatic ringing machine: the frames are of gunmetal, and all steel parts nickel-plated; the pins in the barrel can be easily shifted, when worn, by loosening a screw, a great improvement over the old system. It has fourteen bells, upon the tuning of which the firm pride themselves.
> A model of their patent carrillon machine with seven tunes to each barrel, the barrels being interchangeable. Model of Willing's Jubilee Tower, Brighton, standing about five feet high, showing time on four dials. A ball is raised at seven minutes to the hour, and falls at the hour, actuated by hydraulic pressure. A very nicely finished striking movement, with lever escapement, is fitted in the base. A bell weighing 21/2 cwt., turned inside and out, of fine tone, and fixed to a stand that shows it off to advantage. Another model in brass of a cathedral with a musical box fitted inside. A chronoscope, and several specimens of smaller clockwork.

You will note that the chronoscope is mentioned again.

1889   *The Paris Exhibition*
Although a major exhibition, England had only four chronometer makers there, Kullberg, of course, Usher & Cole, Parkinson & Frodsham and R. Webster. J. Tripplin in his expansive report on the exhibition remarks on pp. 37 and 38: 'English chronometry claims the first place in the world by its finish, performance, and the number produced, although much reduced since the introduction of steamers of quick passage and immense carrying powers still reaching not less than 300 chronometers a year.'

As usual Kullberg came in for well-deserved praise for the superiority of his work from every standpoint, he showed 15 chronometers and received the Grand Prix.

Usher & Cole were mentioned as being not as well-known on the continent as they should be, partly because they so often made for other people. However this position was rectified and they received a gold medal.

The aspects of turret clock manufacture in this exhibition has been covered in that section, the position in this area being more than satisfactory, however, it was mentioned that we lagged behind in the application of electricity in this field. Where domestic clocks were concerned the efforts of the British United Clock Company of Birmingham were recognised. They were praised for establishing the production of cheap drum timepieces with lever escapements, the object being to make England self sufficient in this important branch of the clock trade, a condition that apparently no one dared hope for ten years previous to this exhibition. It is of interest that they also did well at the Melbourne Exhibition of 1889 where they obtained the highest honours for 'your exhibit of nickel and fancy lever clocks, the points being excellence of manufacture, timekeeping qualities, and cheapness. Professor Ellery, the Government Astronomer-Royal, and the other judges, all practical chronometer and watchmakers, were much impressed with the two former points. This award is most important, on account of the strong competition and severe test to which the clocks were subjected.'

J.J. Stockall & Sons were awarded a silver medal for their display of clocks and watches. It was commented that they had made a special study of watchman's tell-tale devices and the installations of electric clock systems. Samuel Smith & Sons received a bronze medal for what was described as the most attractive display in the section. Mappin Brothers also had a bronze medal.

For the first time in the reports I find mention of people called 'collaborators' who received awards. These were obviously the workmen at the various establishments who did so much to make their employers' businesses a success.

The following individuals received a silver medal: L. Sanfrid of Victor Kullberg and Joseph Brown of Usher & Cole. The following a bronze medal: George Abbott of Victor Kullberg; William Renn of Usher & Cole and James Stockall of J.J. Stockall & Sons. The following had an honourable mention: Charles Heap and Ernest Sarter both of S. Smith & Sons Ltd.

1893   The Chicago Exhibition

The *H.J.* this time commented on the fact that there were not many British Manufacturers exhibiting but said that a possible explanation lay in the heavy import duties imposed by America which meant to all intents and purposes that the market was closed to them. On show, however, was a clock by the Goldsmiths & Silversmiths Co. for which they won an award. It was described in the *H.J.* as follows:

> A monumental clock, standing about eight feet high, also by the Goldsmiths' and Silversmiths' Company, is worth attention. The plinth and pedestal are octagonal, the latter bearing representations of different sports, surmounted by medallion portraits of our Queen and seven of the Presidents of America. Above is a square case, showing on four dials English, Chicago, French, and Spanish time. Rising from the pyramidal top of the case is a well-conceived and wrought figure, presumably of Liberty. Between the pedestal and the clock case is a revolving band of figures, but this is, in my judgment, the least admirable feature of the conception.

S. Smith & Sons exhibited and also had an award. They showed long-case and quarter-striking clocks together with a turret movement.

1900   The Paris Exhibition

This is the last exhibition to be covered in this book and in fact shows that things were going downhill. It was reported that the following exhibited: Victor Kullberg, of course, Usher & Cole, The Gold & Silversmiths Co., S. Smith & Son and Stockall.

Usher & Cole obtained another gold medal. Victor Kullberg had the highest honour — The Grand Prix. You will recall that he had gold medals in each of the previous Paris Exhibitions; 1867, 1878 and 1889. The Goldsmiths' Co. showed an Art Nouveau silver-cased clock .

Marine Chronometers were to the fore; England still reigned supreme in this field. There was also a good show of long-case clocks. I quote from the report of the time:

> A fine collection of grandfather clocks in Chippendale, Sheraton, Adams, and old carved oak. The old English styles, which make them all the more impressionable to the foreigner, are not the only styles exhibited, for the Louis styles also form the lines on which other cases in this exhibit are designed. The movements however are genuine British, and have all the characteristics for which the English grandfather clocks are celebrated, — Westminster and Whittington chimes, striking the quarters, Graham dead beat escapement and compensated pendulum. Bracket clocks in all styles and sizes, chiming upon gongs and bells, also find a place in this comprehensive exhibit. Messrs Stockall & Sons have the largest show of English clocks, comprising every style and class of grandfather clock — wood and metal, cased bracket and mantel clocks.

II The Clockmakers' Company and its Masters

The Worshipful Company of Clockmakers is one of the 86 remaining Companies. These Companies are in the main directly descended from the medieval craft guilds. These craft guilds performed a very important function in the past, regulating trade and maintaining standards. London is one of the few places where these guilds or rather their modern equivalent, the Companies, survive. Not, of course, that they perform the same function as they did in the past. The Clockmakers' Company had some illustrious horological names among its members in Victorian times and in fact does to this day. Running through the list of Masters of the Company shows this (see below).

Evidence that the various guilds supervised their respective crafts and trades appears as early as the twelfth century. The main areas of control were the regulation of prices, technical education through apprenticeship and the production of test pieces by these apprentices. There was also inspection of products to ensure a minimum standard and when items were deemed unsatisfactory the pieces could be smashed. There was effectively a closed shop and furthermore the numbers of apprentices were limited. This gave the guilds a virtual monopoly, for their powers were limitless to all intents and purposes. However, almost everybody gained from these associations, the customer was protected against shoddy goods, the members from low prices and an erosion of their standards of living. There was even a certain degree of protection against hard times should a member be unfortunate.

By the seventeenth century the guilds began to lose their grip on things as trade began to expand and it was this concern about competition from abroad that led to the formation of a number of new guilds in the City of London, and among these was the Clockmakers' Company, as it was eventually to be called. In 1622 there were sixteen clock and watchmakers in London and their trade was beginning to be harmed by 'a multiplicitie of Forreners using theire profession in London'. At this time foreigners did not necessarily mean aliens but merely those who were not Freemen living in the City or its suburbs. One source of trouble, however, were the Huguenots, refugees from religious persecution in France. They had arrived in numbers exceeding their counterparts in London.

In the early seventeenth century the Freeman clockmakers of the City had obtained their freedom through the Blacksmiths' Company but it was no longer enough to be a worker in iron, however skilled, to produce portable timekeepers and clockmakers saw the need for a separate identity. After a difficult period the clockmakers finally were granted a charter in the reign of Charles I on 22 August 1631.

However, many clockmakers were already free of other Companies to whom they owed allegiance and, after many vicissitudes, in 1765 the Clockmakers' Company was at last successful in obtaining an Act of Common Council which required that all those working at Clockmaking should take the Freedom of the Company.

Those who govern the Company, known as the Court, comprise the Master, three wardens and not less than ten Assistants.

Admission to the Company is by invitation and requires the sponsorship of a member of the Court. The first step is to be admitted (elected) a Freeman and since 1715 women have been accepted in this class. Later on a Freeman can be invited to become a Liveryman which title allows the individual to take part in the official ceremonies of the Company.

The office of Honorary Librarian and Curator of the Company is held by the Librarian of the Guildhall and he is assisted in horological matters by an assistant curator appointed by the Company. Although the Company has never been wealthy enough to own its own hall, it has a large horological library and a fine museum. In 1873 the entire collection was deposited on loan at the Guildhall where they still remain and where they are open for view and study, not just by members of the Company but by the public at large. In the collection is one Victorian clock and five marine chronometers. For those who would like further details of these there is an excellent publication *Clocks and Watches in the Collection of the Worshipful Company of Clockmakers* by Cecil Clutton and Goerge Daniels, London, 1975.

The Company has armorial bearings, these were granted in 1671 and were redesigned in 1967. The Company's motto is *Tempus rerum imperator*: time is the ruler of all things.

The Masters of the Worshipful Company of Clockmakers 1837–1901

1836	FRODSHAM, William James
1837	,, ,,
1838	GRANT, John
1839	,, ,,
1840	GRAVELL, William, Jr
1841	,, ,,
1842	FENN, Joseph
1843	,, ,,
1844	GANTHONY, Richard Pinfold
1845	ATKINS, George
1846	GRANT, John
1847	VULLIAMY, Benjamin Lewis
1848	ADAMS, Francis Bryant
1849	,, ,,

1850	PERRY, John Aldington	1877	CROLL, Col. Alexander Angus
1851	,, ,,	1878	PARKER, William
1852	HARKER, George	1879	WING, William
1853	,, ,,	1880	WELLBOURNE, Charles
1854	ADAMS, James	1881	ATKINS, Samuel Elliott
1855	FRODSHAM, Charles	1882	ADAMS, James Scovell
1856	CARTER, John (Alderman)	1883	ISAAC, Saul
1857	ADAMS, James	1884	CROLL, Col. Alexander Angus
1858	GRANT, John	1885	THOMPSON, Edward John
1859	CARTER, John (Lord Mayor, 1859–60)	1886	ADAMS, Herbert Jordan
1860	ROWLANDS, William	1887	DYMOND, John Neate
1861	ADAMS, George William	1888	SAVORY, Sir Joseph (Alderman)
1862	FRODSHAM, Charles	1889	ATKINS, Samuel Elliott (Alderman's Deputy)
1863	FENN, Joseph	1890	SAVORY, Sir Joseph Bt (Lord Mayor 1890—1)
1864	CARTER, John		
1865	ADAMS, Francis Bryant	1891	CLARKE, Daniel
1866	ADDISON, John Garrett Curtis	1892	NELTHROPP, Rev. Henry Leonard
1867	ROWLANDS, William	1893	,, ,,
1868	GRANT, John	1894	THOMPSON, Edward John
1869	ADAMS, George William	1895	FENN, Joseph
1869	LAWLEY, William	1896	ATKINS, Charles Edward
1870	MOORE, George	1897	ADAMS, Herbert Jordan
1871	ADDISON, John Garrett Curtis	1898	CARTER, John William
1872	WING, William	1899	ABBOTT, Joseph William
1873	WELLBOURNE, Charles	1900	CRONIN, Walter Daniel
1874	LAWLEY, William	1901	CHRISTIE, William Henry Mahoney (Astronomer Royal)
1875	MOORE, George		
1876	ADAMS, James Scovell		

III   Clockmakers to the Queen

Not unnaturally to hold the Royal Appointment was as important in the Victorian era as it is today, if not more so. Prior to 1839 there were only two horological appointees, one for clocks and one for watches. The picture is not always as clear as it might be and I will be concerned with the makers of watches, chronometers and clocks, since it is not always easy to say what the appointment was for.

Benjamin Vulliamy was the man who looked after the clocks at Buckingham Palace until he died in 1854. During the period 1839 until 1843 he shared the appointment with Sigismund Rentzsch and Arnold & Dent.

Rentzsch was originally described as a watchmaker when his first Royal Appointment was signed in 1820 but when it was renewed in 1830 he was designated Clock and Watchmaker. A second renewal took place in 1837 and he was to continue in office until 1857. Despite this fact and the excellence of his surviving work there is no example of Rentzsch's work in the Royal Collections.

In 1841 the picture changed after the demise of the firm of Arnold & Dent in 1840. Dent wrote to Airy in 1840 asking him for a certificate of fitness so that he could apply to the Lord Chamberlain to be appointed. He must have been surprised when Airy wrote back refusing saying that 'I cannot in a formal document separate the acts of the two partners . . . and that the same applies to prevent me from giving any certificate to Mr Arnold'.

A curious situation then arose for despite the fact that Dent was given the Royal Appointment in 1841 the firm of Arnold & Dent retained their appointment until 1843 when John Roger Arnold died. This situation then remained unchanged until 1852 when J. Ogsten joined the select band. There are no examples of Ogsten's work in this volume.

In 1843 E.J. Dent died and in 1854 two Dents joined the appointees, namely Frederick and Richard Edward. From 1855—7, Vulliamy having died, his place was taken by Charles Frodsham.

In 1858 there were two Dents again but not the same two for Richard E. Dent was replaced by Marrianna Fredericka Dent — an early triumph for women's attempts at recognition.

Ogsten also disappeared in this year and the much-disliked John Bennett joined the others bringing the number back to four. In 1860 Frederick Dent died but this did not prevent the firm that bore his name from retaining the Royal Appointment, which they did until 1875.

In 1862 the number again increased to five and for the first time what one might call a Continental influence crept in by virtue of the inclusion of Aubert & Klaftenberger. D.F. Aubert started in Geneva in about 1820 joining C.J. Klaftenberger at 157 Regents Street from 1835 onwards. The firm exhibited in The Great Exhibition of 1851 where, as well as various types of watches, they showed a 2-day marine chronometer and a regulator with remontoire.

In 1864 the number increased to six with the inclusion of a truly foreign firm who were Paris-based with a London office; this was Leroy & Son.

This combination of people was to remain unchanged until 1884 although during this period John Bennett was knighted. This occurred in 1872 although the fact is not acknowledged until 1876 in the Royal Kalendar. In this same year Frederick Dent was dropped. 1885 saw another change when Dent brought the number up to six again.

During the period 1887—93 the firms serving under the Royal Warrant were the same as in the preceeding period with the exception that in the year of 1887 the list included Lund & Blockley.

IV Glossary of Clock-Case Terms

ABACUS The topmost member of a column capital.

ACANTHUS Because of the elegance of its leaves this has been the most favoured foliage represented in decoration since classical times.

ACORNS Used extensively as a motif for FINIAL.

ACROTERIUM A pedestal for a figure.

APPLIQUÉ Decorative brass or silver work applied to the top and other parts of clock cases.

APRON A decorative drop-piece. May be between the feet of a case or the piece attached to the pallet cock of some verge clocks.

ARABESQUE Decoration in low relief or inlay with fanciful intertwining of leaves, scrollwork, etc.

ARABIC NUMERALS The numerals in normal use, i.e. not Roman.

ARCH Referring only to the shape as in arch-top case or arch-top dial.

ARCHITECTURAL STYLE Has a curiously specific meaning when clock cases are spoken of as really being in classical architectural style with a triangular-shaped superstructure usually supported or appearing to be supported by columns.

BALL FOOT A foot of ball shape.

BANDING A strip or band of VENEER in a panel or around a door. The grain of the wood may be across or in line with the banding.

BARLEY TWIST The shape similar to that of barley sugar from which the name is derived. Used of pillars.

BAS-RELIEF Where the carving or casting is in relief as opposed to being incised.

BEAD A small half-round moulding.

BELL TOP Presenting a profile similar to the section of a bell.

BLIND-FRET A decorative carved effect where the base material appears to be covered in FRETwork.

BLOCK FOOT A square section foot of cube proportions or longer.

BLOCK FRONT Where a door or panel projects rather than being let in flush or recessed.

BOLECTION Refers collectively to all the projecting parts of mouldings.

BOMBÉ A design that bulges as in the plinth of many Dutch long-case clocks.

BOSS A rounded projecting ornament similar in appearance to the boss of a shield.

BOULLEWORK Inlay work usually of brass in tortoiseshell but can be of various combinations. Named after André Charles Boulle. Both base and inlay are cut together so that a perfect fit is achieved.

BOULLE, COUNTER The reverse of the above technique accomplished by making use of what would otherwise be discarded when doing BOULLEWORK, i.e. if the boullework was brass in tortoiseshell then the counter boulle would be tortoiseshell in brass.

BOW FRONT A gently curved front, similar in shape to the unstressed bow.

BRACKET FOOT A foot which has the appearance of a small bracket.

BRACTS A decoration in the form of a leaf that bears a flower in its axil.

BREAK ARCH An arch which terminates at each side in a right-angled piece. There are break-arch cases and break-arch dials.

BREAK FRONT Where the front is not an unbroken line, being interrupted by a projection or recess.

BROKEN PEDIMENT When the pediment is broken at the top.

BUN FOOT A flattened ball foot.

BURR As in burr-walnut.

CABOCHON A rounded protrusion.

CABRIOLE The curved leg like a shallow S.

CALENDAR APERTURE The opening in a dial through which the date may be seen.

CALYX A decoration resembling the outer case of a bud.

CANTED CORNERS Sloping corners.

CAPITAL The top part of a column. It may be carved or moulded.

CARCASE The underlying frame of a clock, often oak in the past. VENEER and mouldings are applied to the carcase to make it into a finished case.

CARTOUCHE An applied or engraved piece that resembles a tablet or a scroll unrolled.

CARYATID Sculptured female figures used instead of columns.

CAVETTO A hollow moulding.

CERTOSINA A type of PARQUETRY employing small pieces of inlay to give a geometrical design.

CHAPTER RING The hour circle on the dial.

CHASING The art of engraving on the outside of raised metal work. Often used to 'crisp up' castings and can be done in conjunction with repoussé work.

CHEEKS The upright supports in the case on which the seat-board rests.

CHEESE FOOT Another term for BUN FOOT.

CHEQUER Alternate squares of light and dark wood to give a chequer-board effect.

CHINOISERIE Chinese ornamentation.

CLAW AND BALL A foot formed so as to resemble a claw holding a ball.

CONSOLE An especially long CORBEL BRACKET.

CORBEL BRACKET A bracket that is or has the appearance of being built into a wall.

CORINTHIAN COLUMN A Grecian column with bell-shaped capital with rows of acanthus leaves.

CORNER PIECES Another name for SPANDRELS.

CORNICE The topmost member of a structure, usually a moulding in a clock case — the uppermost member of an ENTABLATURE.

COUNTER BOULLE See BOULLE.

CRESTING The carved addition above the CORNICE, mainly on early long-case clocks.

CROSS BANDING Where the grain of the veneer runs across the length of the wood.

CURL The natural figure in wood grain where a large branch meets the trunk of the tree.

CYMA RECTA An OGEE MOULDING.

DENTILS or DENTICKS A tooth-like ornamentation consisting of small rectangular blocks with spaces between. usually placed below a CORNICE.

DIAL ARCH The arch formed in the case to accommodate an arched dial.

DIAL FRAME The frame that may surround the dial and be revealed once the door has been opened.

DOG TOOTH A repeating ornamentation of pyramid shapes in low relief.

DOLPHIN FRET A metal FRET containing or mainly composed of figures of dolphins usually found on the sides and the top of a lantern clock.

DROP HANDLE A ring hanging from a boss, which may be a LION'S MASK.

DUTCH FOOT A foot that terminates in a bulge.

EBONISING The process whereby a wood is made to resemble ebony by filling, staining and polishing. Many woods are used but close-grained ones, such as apple, cherry, pear, holly and sycamore, should be used for the best results.

EGGSHELL FINISH A matt finish.

ENCARPUS A festoon of fruit and flowers on a frieze.

ENCAUSTIC The art of burning in with heated wax so as to produce a pattern or picture.

ENDIVE SCROLL A scrolling foliage form.

ENRICHMENT The addition of ormulu, inlay, carving and so on.

ENTABLATURE The frieze moulding and CORNICE forming the part above the column and supported by it.

ESCUTCHEON The applied surround to a keyhole.

EXTRADOS The outside curve of an arch. See INTRADOS.

FAN A popular MARQUETRY motif.

FAUN Half man/half goat figure used as a decorative motif.

FAVAS A honeycomb effect.

FEATHER BANDING Another term for HERRINGBONE.

FESTOON Another term for SWAG, a decoration in a curved draped form.

FIDDLE-BACK A figured VENEER similar in appearance to a fiddle-back.

FIELDED When a panel is broken up into smaller panels.

FILIGREE Ornamental work made from wire with interstices.

FINIAL A projecting piece, often the termination to a column. Can be stylised pine cones, acorns, pineapples, balls, spires, tulips and so on.

FLAMEAU FINIAL A finial representing a flaming torch.

FLEMISH FOOT A scroll-type foot.

FLEUR-DE-LIS The French royal symbol. A representation of three iris-shaped parts tied with a narrow band.

FLUTING Grooving of a regular nature. A stopped flute does not run the full length of the surface it is decorating.

FOIL The space between the cusps or points in Gothic tracery. Three cusps: trefoil; four: quatrefoil, etc.

FOLIATED A term with two meanings: the first, when foils are used (see above); and the second, enriched with leaf forms.

FRET Wood or metal that is pierced, often to allow the sound of striking to be heard more clearly.

FRIEZE The middle member between the CORNICE and the supporting column.

GADROON A decoration resembling reeds or inverted flutes.

GALLERY A decorative wood or metal edge often pierced to resemble railings.

GESSO A mixture of parchment size and gilder's whiting which is built up on a groundwork, this often carved. The gesso itself can also be carved and often then gilded.

GILDING (See also MERCURIAL GILDING.) Gold leaf can be applied to almost any surface. The process may be known as water gilding since the gold leaf is laid with a mixture of clear water and parchment size. A much cheaper method of gilding employs gold size; this is known as 'oil gilding'.

GOTHIC The pointed-arch-style period, twelfth to sixteenth century. There was a revival of the Gothic style in the nineteenth century.

GRIFFIN A decorative motif composed of a lion's body with an eagle's head and wings.

HERRINGBONE A VENEER cut obliquely into strips and placed in such a manner that the result resembles a herringbone.

HOOD The upper removable portion of the case that houses the mechanism and dial. May lift as in earlier clocks or pull forward.

HUSKS a form of decoration of the Sheraton period. It consists of a row of open seed pods each separated by a ball or seed.

IMPOST The part of the pillar upon which the arch rests.

INCISED ORNAMENT Cut in with a chisel or graver.

INLAYING A general term embracing all those techniques that rely on a ground having some other colour or type of material let down flush into it. See BANDING, INTARSIA, MARQUETRY, PARQUETRY.

INTARSIA Derived from the Latin interserere, to insert, intarsia means the inlaying of one wood into another by chiselling out and then filling.

INTRADOS The underside of an arch.

INVERTED BELL TOP Refers to the bell top where the curves are reversed, concave above, convex below.

JAPANNING An opaque varnished finish usually with gilt decoration in imitation of Chinese lacquer work.

KERF The cut made by a saw.

KETTLE FRONT Where the form takes the shape of the old-fashioned kettle.

KEY PATTERN A FRET pattern.

LACQUER True lacquer work is an Oriental technique but the term is often incorrectly applied to JAPANNING. Lacquer is also the name of a protective finish applied to metal to colour and/or protect it.

LANCET Pointed arch of the thirteenth century or Gothic.

LATTICE Interlaced work resembling network in wood or metal.

LIGNUM VITAE A hard, dark, dense wood from the West Indies. Sometimes used in the seventeenth century in place of ebony for VENEER. Because of the waxiness it has self-lubricating properties, and John Harrison used it for pallets, bearings and as the trundles of his lantern pinions. Still used today as the upper bearing of a diamond lap.

LIMED OAK Oak treated with lime to give it a whitish-grey appearance.

LION'S MASK AND RING HANDLES A decorative handle formed of a lion's head with the ring clenched in its teeth.

LOTUS LEAF A decorative motif based on the lotus water-flower.

LOW RELIEF Shallow carving where the detail is raised up; see also BAS-RELIEF.

LOZENGE A diamond-shaped pattern.

MACHICOLATION A space between CORBEL BRACKETS which support a parapet.

MAHOGANY Although used in furniture from about 1730, mahogany was rarely used for clock cases until the middle of the eighteenth century. It was first imported from the West Indies and was very hard, straight-grained and dark in colour. Soon Cuban mahogany, which is finely figured, came into use, followed later in the century by Honduras mahogany. This is of more open grain, of a higher colour and not as well figured as Cuban mahogany. Country clocks, although appearing to be of mahogany, can often be of cherry or pear which can be made to closely resemble it.

MARQUETRY A word of French origin coming from the word marqueter, to spot, to mark. It is applied to the technique where different sheets are cut simultaneously and then fitted one into the other.

MASK An impression of a face used as a form of decoration.

MEDALLION A motif in the shape of a plaque or medal, may be of PARQUETRY, or figures or heads in LOW RELIEF.

MERCURIAL GILDING Also known as fire gilding. Where an amalgam of gold and mercury is applied to the part to be gilded. After washing off the excess the article is heated to drive off the mercury, leaving a durable gilding whose colour varies according to that of the base metal, the finish and the gold used. This process is illegal in many places owing to the extreme danger from the mercury fumes. See ORMOLU.

MODILLIONS Projecting decorative brackets under the CORNICE of a column.

MOSAIC A pattern or picture formed of many minute pieces of marble, gems, etc., of various colours.

MUNTIN The central vertical member of a door, that part of a door which divides the panels.

NECKING The small band or moulding near the top of a column.

OBELISK An upright tapering column with a pyramidal top.

OGEE MOULDING A moulding of double curvature, concave below, convex above.

OIL FINISH A finish achieved by several applications of boiled linseed oil.

ORMOLU Originally bronze fire-gilded, often used nowadays to describe any gilded metal piece.

OUTSET COLUMNS Projecting columns.

OYSTER A circular grain formation from cross-sections of small branches of wood, for example olive, to mention the most commonly used of the woods for this purpose.

PAD FOOT A form of foot usually associated with the CABRIOLE leg.

PARQUETRY, MARQUETRY formed into geometric as opposed to naturalistic shapes.

PATERA Round or oval flat decorative motifs carved or inlaid, often applied loosely to rosettes and other flat ornaments.

PATINA The finish resulting from long exposure to the elements or from countless polishings.

PEDIMENT Used loosely in horology to refer to the structure above the CORNICE.

PERPENDICULAR STYLE A style where the perpendicular lines are emphasised.

PIE-CRUST EDGING A decorative carved edging resembling that given to a pie crust.

PILASTER A pillar attached to a surface or corner, that is, not free-standing.

PLINTH That section of the case below the trunk.

POLLARD A tree that has had its boughs and trunk lopped, causing peculiar growths at the top, which yields a figured wood that can be cut as VENEER.

PORTICO TOP Alternative name for the pediment of an architectural-style case.

PULVINATED FRIEZE Frieze which is cushion-like; pillowy; bulging.

PUTTO A cherub. When associated with decoration it means a representation of a cherub; the plural is putti.

QUATREFOILS See FOIL.

QUIRK An acute sharp-edged groove at the side of a bead or moulding.

REEDING Small parallel rounded elements resembling reeds used on columns or as mouldings.

REPOUSSÉ Ornamental metalwork hammered into relief from the reverse side.

RESERVE Space on an engraved or matted surface left plain to accommodate an inscription.

RIBBON DECORATION A form of decoration resembling ribbon.

RIBBON STICK A form of decoration resembling ribbon wound around a stick.

ROCOCO A style of decoration based on C scrolls with flowing foliage, rocks and shells. A term also used to define an over-abundance of ornament, a frivolous development of the Baroque.

ROE A type of figure in wood of a spotty appearance not unlike shagreen.

SATIN FINISH A dull finish to French polish and a fine straight-grain finish to metalwork.

SCALLOP or SCOLLOP A representation of an escallop shell in carving or MARQUETRY.

SCOTIA A hollow moulding.

SCROLL FOOT See FLEMISH FOOT.

SCROLL ORNAMENT A form of ornamentation resembling a roll of parchment.

SERPENTINE When the lines of a vertical surface are, in plan, curved in and out, that is, of serpentine shape.

SKIRTING Board fixed round bottom of clock case.

SPADE FOOT Another name for BLOCK FOOT.

SPANDREL The space left between a circle and a surrounding square. This space may be decorated by engraving (engraved spandrels), or fitted with applied decorative pieces, in which case these are also called spandrels.

SPRUNG MOULDING Referring to a moulding which is sprung to force it to take up the shape of a curve.

STRAPWORK A style of decoration resembling straps which are curved, interlaced, etc. May be engraved, inlaid or fretted.

STRINGING Thin inlay running in lines of a wood of contrasting colour to the ground wood.

SUNK PANEL Where a panel is beneath the level of what surrounds it.

SWAG A hanging form of decoration such as a drapery or festoons of flowers.

TERM A bust in continuity with its pedestal.

TERMINAL The finishing piece to a post or standard.

TERN FOOT A foot with a three-scroll pattern.

THERM A trunk pillar or pedestal small at the base and larger at the top — a sort of inverted obelisk.

TORCHILUS An alternative name for a SCOTIA.

TORTOISESHELL The shell of the hawksbill turtle, now an endangered species.

TORUS A large bead, one of the classical mouldings.

TRACERY FRETWORK in stone, wood or metal.

TREFOIL See FOIL.

TREILLAGE Trelliswork.

TRUNK The body or main part of the case of the long-case clock. The case has three main parts: TRUNK, HOOD and PLINTH.

TWIST PILLAR Another name for the BARLEY-TWIST pillar.

TYMPANUM The triangular space forming the field of an architectural pediment.

URN FINIAL A FINIAL in the shape of an urn.

VENEER The sheet of wood used to cover another wood, usually finely figured. Early veneers are a minimum of $1/16$ in thick (1.5 mm) as they could only be produced by sawing. Veneers are now produced on a machine using a long skiving blade.

VIGNETTE An ornamentation resembling vine leaves and tendrils.

Bibliography

Abbreviations
H.J. = *The Horological Journal*, the organ of the British Horological Institute.
A.H. Journal = *Antiquarian Horology Journal*.

Aked, C.K., *Conspectus of Electrical Timekeeping*, n.p., 1976.

Allix, Charles, *Carriage Clocks*, London, 1974.

Baillie, G.H., *Clocks and Watches: an historical bibliography*, London, 1951.

Baillie, G.H., *Watchmakers and Clockmakers of the World*, 3rd edn, London, 1951 (vol. 2, see Loomes).

Bain, A., *Alexander Bain's Short History of the Electric Clock*, London, 1852, ed. Hackmann, reprinted 1973.

Barder, R., *English Country Grandfather Clocks*, Newton Abbot, 1983.

Barker, D., *Arthur Negus Guide to English Clocks*, London, 1980.

Basserman-Jordan, Ernst von, *The Book of Old Clocks and Watches*, rev. by Hans von Bertele, London, 1964.

Bates, K., *Clockmakers of Northumberland and Durham*, Rothbury, 1980.

Beeson, C.P.C. *Clockmaking in Oxfordshire 1400–1850*, Enfield, 1962.

Bellchambers, J.K., *Devonshire Clockmakers*, Totnes, 1962.

Bellchambers, J.K., *Somerset Clockmakers*, Totnes, 1968.

Bird, Anthony, *English House Clocks, 1600–1850*, Newton Abbot, 1973.

Britten, F.J., *Horological Hints and Helps*, London, 1934.

Britten, F.J., *The Watch and Clock Maker's Handbook, Dictionary and Guide*, 16th edn, rev. and enlarged by Richard Good, London, 1976.

Britten, F.J., *Old Clocks and Watches and their Makers*, 9th edn, rev. and enlarged by Cecil Clutton, London, 1982.

Bruton, Eric, *Antique Clocks and Clock Collecting*, London, 1974.

Bruton, Eric, *The Longcase Clock*, New York and Washington, 1968.

Chamberlain, Paul M., *It's About Time*, New York, 1941, reprinted London 1964.

Cipolla, Carlo, *Clocks and Culture: 1300–1700*, London, 1967.

Clutton, Cecil and Daniels, George, *Clocks and Watches in the Collection of the Worshipful Company of Clockmakers*, London, 1975.

Daniell, F.M.A., *Leicestershire Clockmakers*, rev. edn, Leicester, 1975.

De Carle, D., *British Time*, London, 1947.

De Carle, D., *Clocks and their Values*, London, 1975.

De Carle, D., *Teach Yourself Horology*, London, 1965.

De Carle, D., *Watch and Clock Encyclopaedia*, London, 1984.

Denison, Edmund Becket, *Clocks, Watches and Bells*, London, 1850 (7th edn 1883).

Dowler, G., *Gloucestershire Clock and Watchmakers*, Chichester, 1984.

Elliott, D.J., *Shropshire Clock and Watchmakers*, London, 1979.

Gazeley, W.J., *Clock and Watch Escapements*, London, 1956, reprinted 1977.

Gazeley, W.J., *Watch and Clock Making and Repairing*, London, 1958, reprinted 1976.

Gould, Rupert T., *The Marine Chronometer: its history and development*, London, 1923, reprinted 1971.

Gillgrass, A., *The Book of Big Ben*, London, 1946.

Hawkins, A.J. *Watch and Clockmakers of Wigan*, Wigan, 1950.

Hawkins, J.B., *Thomas Cole and Victorian Clockmaking*, n.p., 1975.

Haswell, J. Eric, *Horology: the science of time measurement and the construction of clocks, watches and chronometers*, London, 1928, reprinted 1975.

Hope-Jones, F., *Electrical Timekeeping*, London, 1976.

Hope-Jones, F., *Electric Clocks*, London, 1950.

Hope-Jones, F., *Electric Clocks and Chimes*, London, 1976.

Hope-Jones, F., *Electric Clocks and How to Make Them*, London, 1977.

Howse, Derek, *Greenwich Time*, Oxford, 1980.

Jagger, Cedric, *The World's Great Clocks and Watches*, London, 1977.

Joy, Edward T., *The Country Life Book of Clocks*, London, 1967.

Kelly, Alison, 'A Clockmaker's Taste for Ceramics', *Country Life*, 15 June 1967.

Lloyd, H. Alan, *The Collector's Dictionary of Clocks*, London, 1964.

Lloyd, H. Alan, *The English Domestic Clock – its Evolution and History*, London, 1938.

Loomes, B., *Watchmakers and Clockmakers of the World*, vol. 2, London, 1976 (see Baillie).

Loomes, B., *Westmorland Clocks and Clockmaking*, Newton Abbot, 1984.

Loomes, B., *Yorkshire Clockmakers*, Clapham, 1972.

McCrea, *The Royal Greenwich Observatory*, H.M.S.O., London, 1975.

McKenna, J., *Watch and Clockmakers of Warwickshire*, Birmingham, n.d.

Mason, B., *Clock and Watchmaking in Colchester*, London, 1969.

Mather, H.H., *Clocks and Watchmakers of Nottinghamshire*, Nottingham, 1979.

Mercer, Dr. V., *Edward John Dent and his Successors*, Ticehurst, 1977. *Supplement*, 1984.

Mercer, Dr. V., *The Frodshams*, Ticehurst, 1981.

Mercer, Dr. V., *John Arnold and Son*, London, 1972.

Miles Brown, H., *Cornish Clocks and Clockmakers*, Newton Abbot, 1980.

Miller, L. and Hagger, A., *Suffolk Clocks and Clockmakers*, n.p., 1974, *Supplement*, 1979.

Nicholls, A., *Clocks in Colour*, Poole, 1975.

Nicholls, A., *The English Bracket Clock*, Poole, 1982.

Nicholls, A. and Good, R., *Clocks and Watches*, Poole, 1985.

Norgate, J. and M. and Hudson, F., *Dunfermline Clockmakers*, Dunfermline, 1972.

Osborne, C. and Heap, J., *Essex Clock and Watchmakers*, London, 1979.

Penfold, S., *Clockmakers of Cumberland*, London, 1977.

Pickford, C. (ed.), *Turret Clocks*, Ticehurst, 1981.

Ponsford, C.N., *Devon Clocks and Clockmakers*, London, 1985.

Ponsford, C.N., *Time in Exeter*, Exeter, 1978.

Ponsford, C.N., Scott, J.G.M., Authers, W.P., *Clocks and Clockmakers of Tiverton*, London, 1977.

Rare Carriage Clocks, Asprey & Co. Ltd, catalogue 1980.

Reid, L., *North Country Clockmakers*, Newcastle on Tyne, 1925, reprinted 1981.

Roberts, D., *The Bracket Clock*, Newton Abbot, 1982.

Robinson, T. *The Longcase Clock*, Ticehurst, 1981.

Royer-Collard, F.B., *Skeleton Clocks*, London, 1969.

Shenton, A. and Shenton, R., *The Price Guide to Clocks, 1840–1940*, Woodbridge, 1977.

Smith, A. (ed.), *International Dictionary of Clocks*, London, 1979.

Smith, A., *Clocks and Watches*, London, 1975.

Smith, Eric P., *Clocks, Their Working and Maintenance*, Newton Abbot, 1977.

Smith, Eric P., *Striking and Chiming Clocks*, Newton Abbot, 1985.

Smith, John, *Old Scottish Clockmakers*, London, 1921.

Snell, M., *Clocks and Clockmakers of Salisbury*, Salisbury, 1986.

Tebbutt, L., *Stamford Clocks and Watches*, Stamford, 1975.

Tribe, T. and Whatmoor, P., *Dorset Clocks and Clockmakers*, Oswestry, 1981.

Tyler, E.J., *The Clockmakers of Sussex*, Ashford, 1986.

Walker, J.E.S., *Hull and East Riding Clocks*, Hull, 1982.

Horological Book Specialists

Charles Allix and Associates, 32 Bury St, St. James's, London.

G.K. Hadfield, Rock Farm, Chilcote, Swadlincote, Derbyshire.

Rogers Turner Books Ltd, 22 Nelson Road, London SE10 *and* 24 Rue du Buisson Richard, 78600 le Mesnil-le-Roi, France.

Rita Shenton, 142 Percy Road, Twickenham, Middx.

Index of Clockmakers

General Index